Prehistoric life and Evolution

DOUGAL DIXON

PRENTICE HALL

New York   London   Toronto   Sydney   Tokyo   Singapore

PREHISTORIC LIFE AND EVOLUTION

Managing Editor: Lionel Bender
Art Editor: Ben White
Assistant Editor: Madeleine Samuel
Project Editor: Graham Bateman
Production: Clive Sparling

Media Conversion and typesetting
Peter MacDonald and Partners and
Brian Blackmore

AN ANDROMEDA BOOK

Devised and produced by:
Andromeda Oxford Ltd
11–15 The Vineyard
Abingdon
Oxfordshire OX14 3PX
England

Prepared by Lionheart Books

Library of Congress Catalog Card
Number: 91-66998

ISBN 0-13-678319-8

Published in North America by:
Prentice Hall General Reference
15 Columbus Circle
New York, New York 10023

PRENTICE HALL and colophon are
registered trademarks of Simon &
Schuster, Inc.

Origination by Alpha Reprographics
Ltd,
Harefield, Middx, England
Manufactured in Singapore

10 9 8 7 6 5 4 3 2 1

First Prentice Hall Edition

CONTENTS

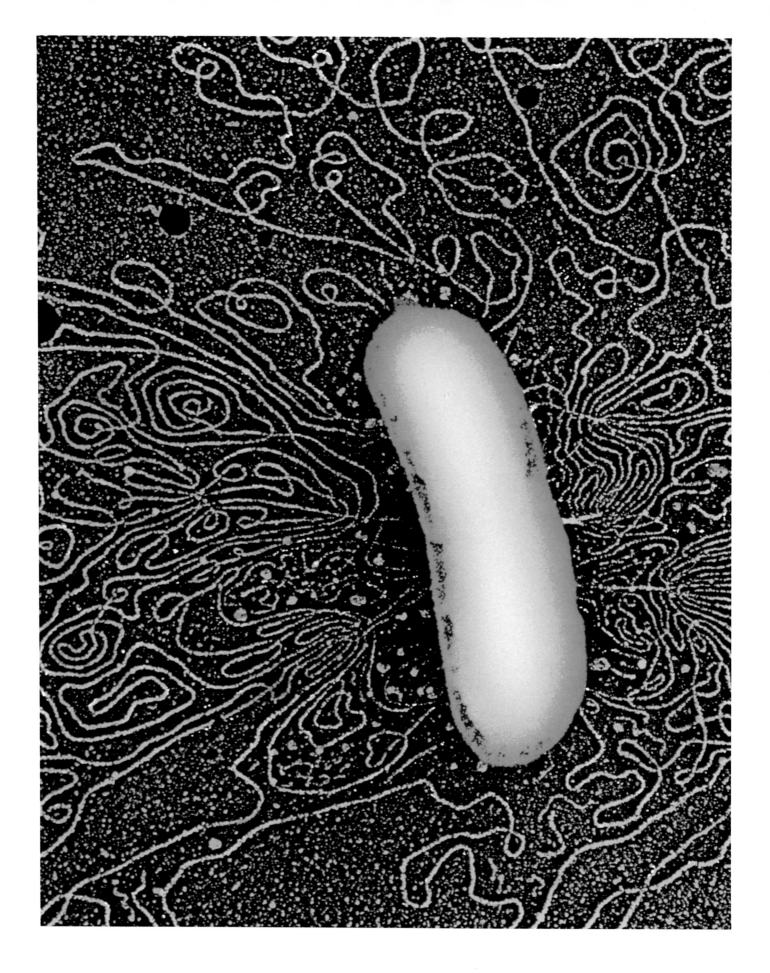

INTRODUCTION

In biology – the study of living things – evolution is the process of gradual change in the characteristics of populations or species that takes place as one generation gives rise to another. The creatures we know today are the result of evolution that has been taking place over 3,000 million years since life on Earth first arose. This book looks primarily at the evolution of animals but it also highlights the major changes in plant life.

The first section of the book surveys the major geological changes that have taken place on Earth over the past 4,000 million years. It describes how these have led to various creatures, such as the dinosaurs, dying out and how their remains have formed fossils. It explains how palaeontologists – scientists who study fossils – have interpreted these to produce the various theories of evolution. Charles Darwin's theory of evolution by the process of natural selection is dealt with in detail.

The next section deals with the origins of life on Earth, the process of adapting to changes in the environment, and the likely course of events in the evolution of all the different types of animals. The third, and largest, section describes in turn the eras and periods in geological time and the wildlife associated with each of them. Within this section are articles dealing with

evolution of the major groups of animals, from invertebrates – animals without a backbone – to fish, reptiles, amphibians, birds and mammals. The last articles deals with evolution of the human species.

Each article in this book is devoted to a specific aspect of the subject. The text starts with a short scene-setting story that highlights one or two of the topics described in the article. It then continues with details of the most interesting aspects, illustrating the discussion with specific examples.

Within the main text and photo captions in each article, the common or everyday names of animals and plants are used. For species illustrated in major artworks but not described elsewhere, the common and scientific (Latin) names of species are given in the caption accompanying the artwork. The index, which provides easy access to text and illustrations, is set out in alphabetical order of common names and of animal and plant groupings with the scientific names of species shown in parentheses.

A glossary provides definitions and short explanations of important technical terms used in the book. There is also a Further Reading list giving details of books for those who wish to take the subject further.

◄An electron microscope photograph of the DNA contents of a bacterium, *Escherichia coli*, spilling out of the cell. This genetic material specifies all the characteristics of the bacterium.

GEOLOGY AND ANCIENT LIFE

The clergyman is puzzled. He looks at the stone shells embedded in the rocks in the disused quarry. Surely, once upon a time, these rocks were muddy particles at the bottom of the sea, and these shells were creatures that lived in them. The Bible says nothing about things like this. The time that is supposed to have passed since the Creation could not have accounted for these changes. Perhaps there is more to the history of the world than is mentioned in the Bible. He must keep his eyes and mind open to new ideas. There is so much to be found out about the world.

People used to think that the Earth was only a few thousand years old. In AD 1650 Archbishop Usher of Ireland added up all the years that were accounted for in the Old Testament of the Bible and came up with the date of 4004 BC as the date of the Creation. In his system the date of the great Flood was 2349 BC. Meanwhile, people in other countries had been coming up with totally different timescales based on their own religions and traditions. But all of them believed that the Earth was thousands, and not millions, of years old.

However, throughout history some people had been trying to interpret the life-like forms and geological formations that they saw in rocks by comparing them to contemporary objects and conditions on Earth. In ancient Greece for example, about 450 BC, the historian Herodotus thought that the presence of fossil shells far inland meant that the seas had been in different positions in times past.

ENLIGHTENMENT DAWNS

By the 17th century, it was increasingly accepted by scientists that fossils were indeed the remains or impressions of once-living things hardened in rock, and not sports of nature or creations of the Devil. It became obvious that the Earth was much older than had previously been thought. Many fossils were unlike anything living at the time, and so people began to realize

▼ The beginning and the end of the world have always held a fascination, as shown by *The Great Day of His Wrath* painted by the English artist John Martin (1789–1894).

that different creatures lived on Earth at different times in the past, and then became extinct. It was also clear that the history of the Earth and of the changes in life-forms on the planet were inter-linked.

The development of knowledge of the formation and structure of the Earth was not a steady build-up of valid discoveries. There were plenty of incorrect ideas as well. At the end of the 18th century, Abraham Gottlob Werner (1750–1815), a German professor of mining, looked at the rocks of the Earth and guessed that they had all been produced in an ancient hot ocean. This became known as the Neptunian Theory. The mineral crystals in such rocks as granite gave him this idea. Contemporary scientists, such as the Frenchman Nicolas Desmarest (1725–1805), put forward the Plutonic Theory. This stated that most rocks were originally molten and then solidified. We now know that the truth lies between the two – some rocks were laid down in water, while others solidified from hot molten material.

THE PRESENT-DAY THEORY

The founder of modern geology, or Earth science, is generally regarded to be the Scottish geologist James Hutton (1726–1797). In 1785 he put forward the idea that the Earth is continually undergoing changes. The landscape is constantly breaking down, with rocks being worn away by the weather, and soils being washed down to the sea. There the rocky debris is laid down in layers, which are eventually buried and turned to rock. Rocks made from such debris or sediment – particles of sand, gravel, mud and silt – are known as sedimentary. At the same time, other parts of the landscape are being pushed up as new mountains. Underneath these, new rocks are forming as molten material from the Earth's interior rises to the surface, cools and solidifies. This type of rock is called

▲ The Bible tells us of the Great Flood that wiped out the wicked people of the world many years ago, here depicted in a painting by English artist Francis Darby (1793–1861). When fossils of extinct animals were found, it was often thought that they had been killed by the Flood. Then scientists began to think that there had been more than one flood.

▼ In the 18th century, the contorted rocks that are exposed in cliff faces were finally recognized for what they were – layers or "beds" of mud and sand laid down at the bottom of the sea and eventually turned to stone. Earth movements twisted them and lifted them up into mountain ranges. In a sequence like this the youngest bed was at the top.

igneous. A third type of rock, known as metamorphic, is formed as sedimentary and igneous rocks are crushed and cooked deep within mountains until they have a highly modified composition and texture.

This constant formation and wearing away of rock is the basis for the modern science of geology and it is on this theory that an understanding of fossils is based.

THE FOSSIL MYSTERY

Once it was accepted that fossils were the remains of living things, scientists began to wonder why some fossils were so different in shape and form from the plants and animals they could see around them. Obviously there were creatures that lived on the Earth in times gone by and that died out. But why did they become extinct?

One of the earliest theories, and one that was popular in the early 19th century, was that there were many great disasters and catastrophes, like the biblical Flood, during Earth's history. Each catastrophe wiped out all living things and life was created again immediately afterwards. A few other theories held that the changes were due to the fact that life was constantly and gradually changing. The changes were too slow to be seen within a person's lifetime, but their timescale was short compared to the age of the Earth. This was the first glimmer of the idea of evolution.

HOW EVOLUTION OCCURS

It is the English naturalist Charles Darwin (1809–1882) who is regarded as the founder of the evolutionary theory. But many other scientists had,

▲Charles Darwin (left) and Alfred Russel Wallace (right) both created the idea of natural selection. Each did so after studying exotic wildlife on scientific expeditions. Darwin's observations were made on the voyage of *H.M.S. Beagle* that sailed round the world between 1831 and 1836. Wallace's were made mostly in the islands of the East Indies. There was no rivalry between the two and Wallace was happy to let Darwin take the fame.

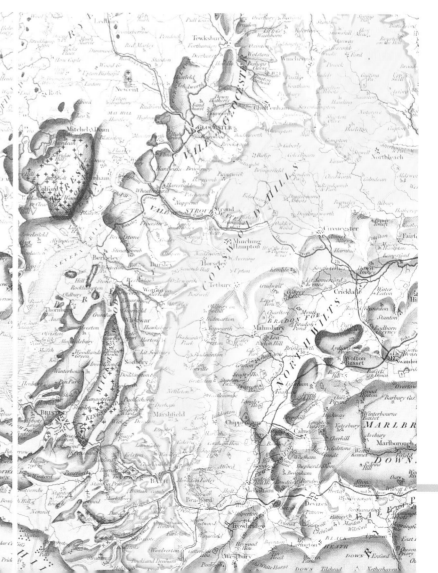

▲▶William Smith (1769-1839), an English canal engineer, was the first to put fossils to a practical use. While excavating canals in southern England, he recognized that different sets of fossils lay in different beds of rock. He found that he could date any rock sequence by looking at the fossils it contained. The same technique is used by modern geologists. This led Smith to produce the first geological maps, with each rock outcrop colored according to its age.

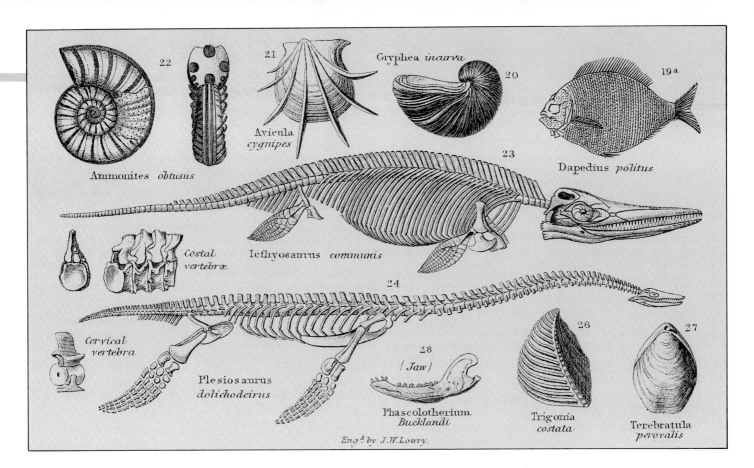

Ammonites *obtusus*

Avicula *cygnipes*

Gryphea *incurva*

Dapedius *politus*

Costal *vertebræ*

Icthyosaurus *communis*

Cervical *vertebra*

Plesiosaurus *dolichodeirus*

[Jaw]

Phascolotherium *Bucklandi*

Trigonia *costata*

Terebratula *perovalis*

Eng.ᵈ by J.W.Lowry.

▲In the 19th century fossils and geology became popular, and many books on the subjects were published.

▶The first scientific restorations of fossil animals, like this Giant ground sloth, were made in Victorian times.

by the same period that Darwin was studying the subject, come to the firm conclusion that evolution had actually taken place. It was Darwin, though, along with his contemporary, a Welsh naturalist called Alfred Russel Wallace (1823–1913), who came up with an idea of the process that produced evolutionary changes. This process he called natural selection.

The basic principle behind natural selection is that when an animal or a plant reproduces, the offspring are essentially the same as the parent. Occasionally, however, an offspring differs in some appreciable way, perhaps in its size, color or its ability to digest a type of food. This difference is called a mutation. Usually the mutation is harmful, and makes it difficult for the offspring to survive. Such a mutation usually disappears very quickly from a population of individuals. Occasionally the mutation is such that it gives the offspring some advantage over its fellow creatures. When this happens the offspring survives and has offspring of its own. These new offspring, being similar to their parent, will still have that mutation. Over several generations, the numbers of individuals in the population bearing the mutation will grow. As other beneficial mutations occur, over millions of years a new species will eventually arise.

HEREDITY AND GENES

Darwin did not know why these mutations arose, but at the time that he was working on his ideas there was other research being done that would eventually reveal the secret. Gregor Mendel (1822–1884), a monk living in what is now Czechoslovakia, was breeding peas and calculating how the numbers of different types in a population changed from generation to generation. His work was not well-known at the time, but early in the 20th century his results were rediscovered. They became the foundation of the modern science of genetics.

We now know that an individual's characteristics – its structure and appearance and so on – are based on a mixture of instructions, called genes, which are inherited from both its father and mother. The genes are the result of the arrangement of special molecules in microscopic thread-like structures, the chromosomes, inside an organism's cells. A random change in this arrangement of molecules will produce a mutation, and this will survive or die out through the process of natural selection.

HISTORY IN THE ROCKS

An important aspect of understanding evolution is to look at fossils and work out what kind of animals and plants existed in prehistoric times. Another is to examine the rocks that contain the fossils and establish what kind of world the ancient creatures lived in. The types and arrangements of the sedimentary rocks and the geological structures found in them can tell us how they were laid down and what the environments were like at that time. This study is called stratigraphy or historical geology.

LAYER UPON LAYER

A river is in flood. The waters are brown and thick with the rock debris, silt and sand swept along by the turbulent currents. This suspension is carried out to sea. In the open ocean the river currents die away and the suspension settles to the sea bed and forms "sediment." The heaviest particles – gravel and sand – settle out first. The finer silt floats about for longer and then settles on top. A thick layer of sediment starts to form. Once the flood has died down, this process of sedimentation stops.

For a time there will be only the gradual settling on the sea bed of mud churned up by the waves and ocean currents. A flood the following year produces another layer of sediment on top of the first. Eventually, these layers may be turned into beds of sedimentary rock, separated by distinct dividing lines called bedding planes. The river-current deposits will have sandstone at the bottom, with finer siltstone on top. Then there will be beds of shale, a rock formed from the sea mud.

BENDS AND BREAKS IN ROCK

The Earth's outermost layer of rock, the crust, is constantly in motion. As the continents move to and fro, they jostle against one another and the beds of rock crumple, crack and twist up into mountains. Horizontal beds of rock may form folds, pushing up into arched structures called anticlines. Or they may sag into dips known as synclines. Where a crack forms in a bed and the masses of rock on either side shift along the break, the resulting structure is called a fault. Movement of the rocks along a fault can result in devastating earthquakes.

Increasingly over the past century, geologists have been working back through the many events that have shaped the ancient (and present-day) landscapes. They have established what the rocks were like millions of years ago before they were folded or

▶▼ Sedimentary beds formed from river sediments can be recognized by the curved structures in them (right). A tongue of sand builds out in S-shaped beds (1). The next phase wears off the tops of the S-shapes (2), and builds up another set (3).

▲▼A sequence of folded rocks, like this elegant syncline and anticline in Wales (above), is usually the result of a complex series of geological events. When a mass of sedimentary rocks is compressed from the side, it begins to fold (1). The fold does not produce a gently rounded landscape because the highest part begins to erode, or wear away, immediately, and the debris collects in the hollows (2). This has happened in the Welsh example, where the topmost parts of the syncline have been worn away. Eventually the compression may become so great that the rocks can fold no more and the structure tears into a fault (3). This combination of fold and fault is known as a thrust, and may produce a movement spread over hundreds of miles (4). The result of the continual compression and erosion is a complicated sequence of rocks that is very difficult for the geologist to decipher. The study of rock shapes like these is known as structural geology.

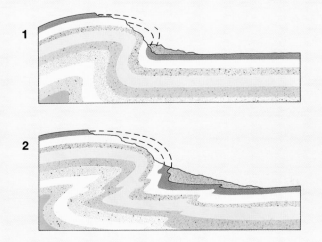

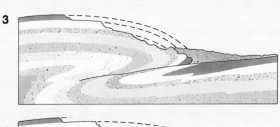

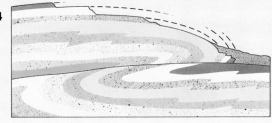

faulted, and they have determined what kinds of sediments formed the rocks. From this they have deduced the kinds of environment that produced the sediments and have traced the history of the Earth's surface over the past 4,000 million years and more.

TIMESCALE AND ERAS

Geological time is measured in hundreds of millions of years. This gives dates that are difficult to comprehend because of the unwieldy numbers of zeros. So geologists divide up the Earth's history into sections, called eras and periods, based on the kinds of creatures that lived at that time.

The first 4,000 million years of Earth's history is called the Precambrian era. Very few fossils are known from this time. The era is divided into two parts: the Archean, in which there was no life, and the Proterozoic, in which simple forms of life did exist.

At the beginning of the next era, the Paleozoic, animals evolved hard shells and skeletons, and fossils are common after this time. Paleozoic history charts the development of life from sea-living organisms to complex creatures that lived on land.

The third era, the Mesozoic, was the time of the dinosaurs and other giant reptiles. Finally, in the last 65 million years, the Cenozoic era, the mammals came to the fore, and this brings us to the present day.

▶The geological timescale was established by the pioneer geologists working in the 19th century. Most work on the Paleozoic rocks was done in Wales and England, which is why the names of the early periods are based on English and Welsh place names and the names of ancient British tribes. The timescale is used worldwide with the only regional variation being in the Carboniferous period, which, in North America, is regarded as two distinct periods, the Mississippian and the Pennsylvanian.

Geological timescale chart

CENOZOIC	Early civilizations
	Emergence of humans
	Start of main Himalayan folding
	Extinction of dinosaurs
MESOZOIC	Main fragmentation of Pangaea; flow of sea over land
	Start of break-up of Pangaea
	Worldwide flow of sea from land
PALEOZOIC	Formation of Pangaea
	Animal life takes to the land
	First land plants
	Major flow of sea over continents
PRECAMBRIAN	First multicellular organisms
	?3000: Free oxygen in atmosphere
	?3500: First unicellular organisms
	3780: Age of oldest known terrestrial rocks
	4600: Formation of Earth
	?10,000: 'Big Bang'

Period	Epoch	Age (million years)
Quaternary	Holocene	0.01
	Pleistocene	2
Tertiary	Pliocene	5
	Miocene	25
	Oligocene	38
	Eocene	55
	Paleocene	65
Cretaceous		144
Jurassic		213
Triassic		248
Permian		286
Carboniferous	Pennsylvanian	320
	Mississippian	360
Devonian		408
Silurian		438
Ordovician		505
Cambrian		590
Proterozoic		2600
Archaean		4600

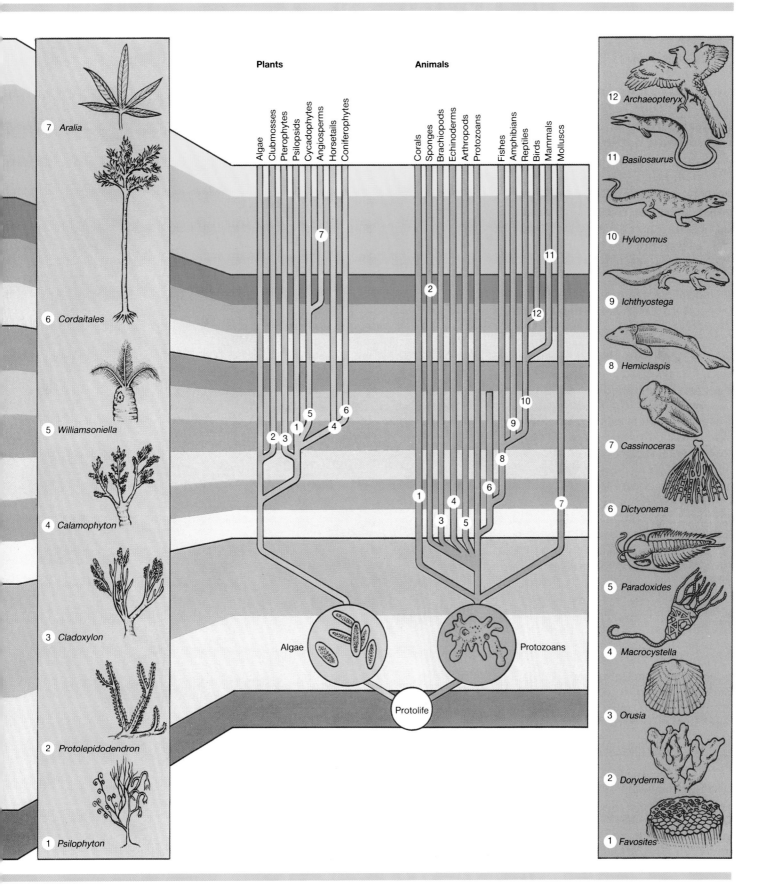

Plants

Algae
Clubmosses
Pterophytes
Psilopsids
Cycadophytes
Angiosperms
Horsetails
Coniferophytes

Animals

Corals
Sponges
Brachiopods
Echinoderms
Arthropods
Protozoans
Fishes
Amphibians
Reptiles
Birds
Mammals
Molluscs

Algae

Protozoans

Protolife

7 Aralia

6 Cordaitales

5 Williamsoniella

4 Calamophyton

3 Cladoxylon

2 Protolepidodendron

1 Psilophyton

12 Archaeopteryx

11 Basilosaurus

10 Hylonomus

9 Ichthyostega

8 Hemiclaspis

7 Cassinoceras

6 Dictyonema

5 Paradoxides

4 Macrocystella

3 Orusia

2 Doryderma

1 Favosites

FOSSILS

The fish died. No longer was its living form seen on the surface of the Earth. The waters swept sand and mud over its body and it became buried. Its soft flesh and internal organs rotted away, but its hard skeleton remained, absorbing the minerals from the rocks round about. Now, 100 million years later, the overlying rocks have fallen away, revealing the fish's shape to the world long after the animal's lifetime.

In the tallest summits of the Himalayas, at up to 29,000 ft the highest mountains on Earth, there are fossils of shells from animals that lived on the bottom of the sea 50 million years ago. And that is not a long time in geological terms. In the middle of the Sahara Desert, one of the world's driest places, lie the fossilized bones of primitive pig-like elephants that wallowed in lush tropical swamps at about the same time. Fossils – the remains or impressions of living things hardened in rock – tell us not only what life was like on Earth in ages gone by, but also how the landscapes and conditions have changed through the vast sweeps of geological time.

AFTER DEATH
How did the fossils in the Himalayas, the Sahara and elsewhere come to be there in the first place? Not many of the creatures that are alive at a particular instant of time are likely to become fossilized. In the normal course of events, an animal (or a plant) dies and then disappears for ever. Scavenging animals come along and eat the meat, tearing apart the dead body, or carcass, and scattering the bones or breaking the shells. Microorganisms, particularly fungi and bacteria, then break down the remains – even the hard parts like bone and horn. The whole body is in this

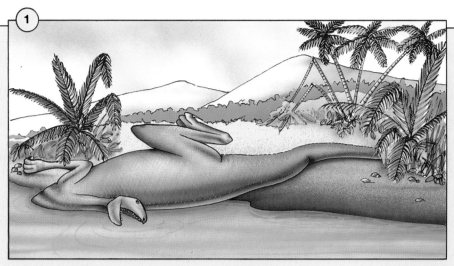

Fossil formation
A fossil is the result of a whole series of events. Through old age, disease, lack of food or a related reason, an animal dies (1). If it falls into water, it may sink and be buried by mud, sand or other sediment (2). More sediment may be piled on top in layers until at last the carcass lies deep underground (3). The muds and sands all around are compressed and the fragments of rock cemented together until they form a sequence of sedimentary rocks. The same geological process will have an effect on the remains of the animal – it is usually just the hard parts that are left – and turn them into fossils (4). They may be embedded in the rock for all time. On the other hand, the particular sequence of rocks may be affected by Earth movements, and the whole area of land thrust up into high mountains. The rocks at the surface will then begin to wear away or erode. Eventually, the rocks will wear down to the level containing the fossils (5).
It is then that we will be able to see the fossils in the rock. The process of erosion is a continuous one, however, and eventually the fossils themselves will wear away along with the rocks that contain them.

Events may happen differently at every stage. The floating carcass may be torn apart by crocodiles or fish; minerals and other chemicals in the rocks may eat away the bones altogether; or the fossils may never be exposed at the surface. The chances of any particular organism becoming a well-formed fossil are millions to one.

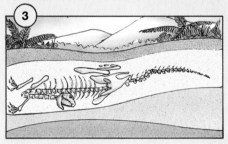

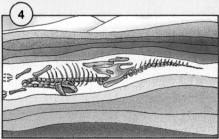

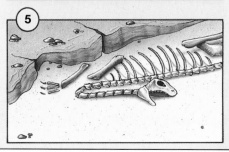

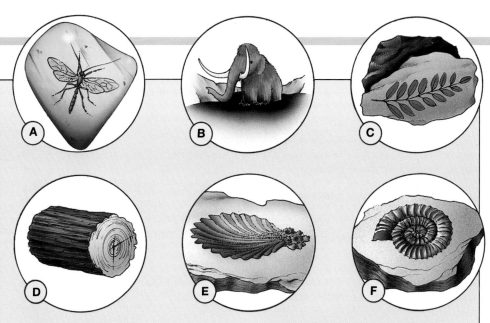

Types of fossil

A fossil can be defined as any trace of a living thing that tells us about conditions on the Earth's surface in times gone by. Usually, during fossilization, an organism has changed in some way since it was a living thing, but not always. Insects in the resin material, amber **(A)**, are preserved in their entirety, and the bones of mammals trapped in tar **(B)** consist of the original bone material. Fossil fern leaves sometimes consist of the original carbon **(C)**. Generally, though, the original substances have been replaced. The process known as petrification

involves the replacement, molecule by molecule, of the original material by a mineral **(D)**. When the organism finally rots away leaving a hole, it produces a mold **(E)**, and when this fills up with sediment, it produces a cast **(F)**.

▼ The removal of a fossil from a rock can be a very painstaking process. A geologist may use a whole tool kit of delicate instruments to pick the fragments of rock away from the specimen. Dental instruments are particularly useful for this work.

way reduced to chemicals that pass into the soil, or the surrounding water, eventually to feed the plants growing in the area. These plants are eaten by plant-eating animals, the herbivores, which eventually die, and so on. The whole unending repetitive process is called the food cycle.

RECORDED IN STONE

In certain circumstances, however, a dead body can stay outside this system. If a creature dies and the carcass cannot be reached by scavenging animals, and if it is sealed off from micro-organisms, then it may be preserved for a long time. One way in which this can happen is if a land animal falls in a river and drowns. Its body will be washed downstream until the current weakens. It will then sink to the river bed and be buried by the sand and silt washed down with it. Nothing can then get at the carcass to eat it, and the bones of the skeleton are held together as the soft parts gradually decay away. Later, as more sand and silt cover the carcass and the sediments turn to rock, the bones may become filled, or impregnated, with minerals, producing a stony substance and turning them to fossils. The whole process takes tens of thousands or millions of years.

FOSSIL RETRIEVAL

The removal of a fossil from the rock can be easy or very difficult depending on a number of varying factors. If the fossil is made of a hard mineral, like silica, and it is embedded in a soft rock, for example shale, then it can be extracted without difficulty. It is separated from the surrounding rock using a hammer and chisel. On the other hand, if the fossil is made of calcite and is embedded in limestone (which is also made of calcite), it will be almost impossible to remove.

If a fossil and its rock are made of different materials, the specimen can be put into an oven and heated. The two materials will expand at different rates. If the rock expands faster, it will separate from the fossil, which can then be lifted out. If the fossil expands faster, however, it will force itself out from the rock.

Sometimes acid is used to eat away the rock from around a fossil, but only after having tested that the acid will not damage the fossil. Large fossils, like dinosaur bones, have to be treated particularly carefully in order to keep them whole during the removal process. They are usually wrapped in plaster as a doctor would protect a broken leg, while they are dug out of the rock and carried to the laboratory or museum for study.

ENTOMBED FOR ALL TIME
An insect alights accidentally on a blob of sticky resin seeping from the trunk of a conifer tree. It is trapped, and the more it struggles the deeper into the resin it sinks. Soon it dies, suffocated by the thick fluid. The tree dies too, and falls to the ground. Eventually the tree is buried in soil and the blob of resin hardens and turns to the semi-precious material amber. All this time, the insect has remained unaltered, sealed in the resin away from any micro-organisms that would decompose it. Its original form can still be seen within the amber.

Sometimes people find the entire corpses of mammoths preserved from the Ice Age 80,000 to 10,000 years ago. People often think of mammoths as being preserved in ice. In fact they are preserved in frozen mud. During the cold climates of the past 2 million years, mammoths roamed the tundra regions of the far north. They scraped away the snow from the ground with their huge tusks to feed on the short grasses and lichens beneath. Once in a while, one of them would break through the surface of a frozen peat bog and sink into the cold liquid mud and drown. The mud would then freeze and preserve the entire corpse.

The first frozen mammoth to be found in Siberia in the Soviet Union was thawing out of a river bank. The people who found it did not recognize it as a kind of elephant, as the wolves had eaten off the trunk. That shows how fresh the meat was!

UNALTERED BONES AND TEETH
Southern California in the United States is rich in oil. Throughout the last few million years the oil has been seeping to the surface of the land, and evaporating away, leaving pools of sticky tar. Large prehistoric animals, like mammoths and Giant ground sloths, blundered into this tar and became stuck. Meat-eaters, for example Saber-toothed tigers, followed them, sensing an easy meal, and became stuck in tar too. Then came the scavengers, for instance condors

▶Ferns more than 300 million years old, like these fronds of *Sphenopteris obtusiloba* from a coal measure, are often preserved as black silhouettes formed of their original carbon atoms.

▲Shells may be sufficiently resistant to decay and erosion to have their original substance preserved intact, but ancient plants have usually been altered.

▶Mammoths, like this youngster, can be found frozen in the icy wastes of the far north, their meat still quite fresh.

and wolves, and these in turn were trapped. Today, the unaltered bones of thousands of these animals can be found in tar pools in the middle of Los Angeles.

Unaltered shark teeth some 50 million years old are found in sea sediments in eastern England. Shark's bones are made of gristle (cartilage), not bone, and easily decay away, but their teeth are tougher and preserve very well.

THE RAW STUFF OF COAL
Usually any soft fleshy parts of an organism decay away, but some of the constituent chemical substances may be left intact. Black shapes of leaves are often found in thinly bedded shale, which is a rock formed from fine-grain sediments. The black substance is the original carbon of the leaf, left

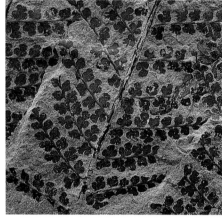

▲ Beautifully preserved insects, such as this wasp (left) and fly (right), are often found in amber in Cenozoic tree fossils by the Baltic Sea. Amber forms from a transparent resin of pine and other trees which hardens with time. They are prized by mineral collectors and jewelers.

behind when the oxygen and hydrogen atoms have been removed by chemical processes. Masses of leaves preserved like this, from now-extinct plants such as giant tree ferns, club mosses and horsetails, form today's coal measures.

ALL SHAPES AND FORMS

You would expect that anything as old as a typical fossilized creature will have altered somewhat since the time when it was a living being. Usually, the vast range of natural processes that take place in the Earth's crust will have acted on the remains in some way and changed them in shape and form. Just as the sediments that are laid down in the sea or the river bed are cemented, compacted and turned into rock, so the remains of living things in the rock are turned into minerals as well.

CELLS INTO STONE

Some of the most beautiful and detailed fossils result from the process known as petrification. Rain, the meltwater from snow and ice, and water from rivers and streams, quickly seep through the soil. As this "groundwater" seeps slowly through the sediments and the rock, it carries with it many dissolved minerals. At certain concentrations and temperatures, these minerals no longer stay in liquid form and instead they develop into solid crystals. In a buried bone or a piece of buried wood, the original living or organic matter may decay away very gradually, and be replaced, molecule by molecule by the mineral. As a result, the microscopic structure of the specimen will be preserved. The cellulose tissues of the wood, for example, may be replaced by silica. Sometimes the replacement is only partial, with some of the original substance remaining, but often the whole mass is replaced.

Silica, the very hard mineral that is the main component of sand and is used to make glass, produces the best petrified fossils. Some of the earliest fossil land plants that we know lie in sandstones in northern Scotland. They grew in the Devonian period, 408 to 360 million years ago, by the side of a desert lake. Suddenly they were engulfed by silica-rich water bursting from a nearby volcano, and the silica preserves to this day the intricate cellular structure of these primitive plants.

FOSSIL TREES IN A DESERT
In Arizona in the southwest of the Unites States there is a national park called Petrified Forest. There, dotted over the desert, are chunks of logs that look quite normal, but in fact they are made of silica. In Triassic times, 248 to 213 million years ago, there were forests of conifer trees nearby. The trees grew by the sides of shallow swamps and sluggish rivers that lay at the foot of a recently formed mountain range. During a flood a number of fallen trees were swept into the area, became wedged in a log jam, and were buried in river sands. Over millions of years, the silica held in the groundwater worked its way into the cells of the wood and turned the logs into hard, weather-resistant fossils. Impurities such as iron and manganese have stained the silica bright colors, and the resulting petrification is as beautiful to look at as polished wood can be.

▲Limestone may be full of fossils of ancient sea creatures such as these ammonites, which are cast in the mineral calcite absorbed from the rock itself.

▶These casts of ammonites are sufficiently detailed to allow geologists to identify the species.

FILLING IN HOLES
Occasionally, when a bone or a shell lies buried in sediments, the seeping water will react chemically with its substance, and dissolve it away without leaving any trace. If, though, the surrounding sediment has, by this time, turned into solid rock, there will be a hollow where the shell used to be. This hollow will be the exact shape of the shell itself. Geologists call this hollow a mold.

A mold is not a great deal of use as a fossil. However, if geologists know that a mold is present, they can use it to produce a solid object that is easier to study and is more instructive. In the Triassic desert sandstones of Scotland, there are molds that represent the skeletons of ancient desert-living reptiles. Scientists have poured latex, a thick liquid rubber, into them through holes drilled through the rock. When the latex solidified, it

produced exact three-dimensional copies of the original bones. These were afterwards broken free of the rock using hammer and chisel.

Archeologists have done the same thing in the ruins of Pompeii, the Roman city that was destroyed in AD 79 when it was buried in ash during the eruption of the nearby volcano Vesuvius. The bodies of people and animals that were engulfed by the ash have decayed away and left molds, and their exact shapes have been reproduced by pouring in plaster to fill the space.

CAST IN ROCK
Solid shapes produced from molds are known as casts. Casts may also form naturally as groundwater deposits minerals which completely fill the space of the mold. These casts differ from petrifications in that they only preserve the outward shape; there is no sign of the original internal structure of the organism.

A special kind of cast forms as sediment fills the space between two closed bivalve shells – as possessed by such marine animals as mussels, scallops and clams – or the interior of a coiled shell of an organism like a water

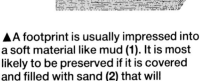
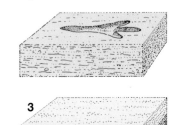

▲A footprint is usually impressed into a soft material like mud (1). It is most likely to be preserved if it is covered and filled with sand (2) that will eventually solidify to sandstone (3).

When the rock is exposed, the soft shale containing the print – like the dinosaur print in the photo above – is worn away, leaving the sandstone cast as a permanent reminder (4).

snail. The shell itself may decay away, but it leaves a cast that represents the inside space. This is called an internal cast. Such casts are often useful because they show the scars where the animal's muscles were once attached.

FOOTPRINTS IN THE SANDS
A fossil may not be the actual remains of a once-living thing. Footprints left by animals drinking at a muddy waterhole and burrows made by worms in sea sediment can be preserved in the beds of sedimentary rock. These marks left in the rocks are referred to as trace fossils.

FUEL AND BUILDING STONE
Fossils are useful for charting the progress of the evolution of life. They can also be put to other, more practical, uses. Carbonized plant material dating from the Carboniferous period forms coal. The Industrial Revolution in Europe of the 18th and 19th centuries was therefore based on fossil plants. Most of today's industries are based on oil (petroleum), and oil is also derived from once-living things. Plant remains trapped in layers of sediment as they formed were decomposed by bacteria. A thick liquid (crude oil) and various gases

hydrocarbons) were produced, and under certain conditions these were trapped in large quantities in beds of rock. By drilling down into the rock, the oil and "natural" gas are extracted.

Some of the best limestones used in buildings consist of nothing but masses of fossil animal shells and skeletons. Often the stones are ground smooth and polished so that the fossils are visible.

FOSSIL TIMEKEEPERS
More importantly for geologists, fossils can be used to determine easily the date of the rocks in which they appear. Over the past century or so,

◀ A mass of dead fish in sandstone from the Devonian period, 408–360 million years ago, tells us of a disaster. The fish were evidently trapped in a pool that was drying up, and they perished quickly.

▼ Trilobites, common fossils from the Paleozoic era, came in many shapes and forms. Most species only existed for a short period of time and then died out. Many species lived together at the same time. If scientists find fossils of the Proetidae and the Agnostida in the same rock, they can tell that the rock formed in Ordovician times since only then did both types exist together.

scientists have found out a great deal about all the most common fossils, including when they lived. The most widely used method of finding the age of fossils is known as radiometry. It consists of comparing the amounts in a fossil of the radioactive and non-radioactive (stable) forms of the atoms of elements such as carbon, uranium and potassium. Given this ratio, and with knowledge of how many years it takes half of the atoms in a sample of the radioactive form to change into the stable form (the half-life), the age of the fossil can be calculated. If scientists see in a rock a fossil that they recognize and have dated from another rock, they can assume that the two rocks were formed at the same time.

The best fossils for this purpose are those of animals that existed throughout the world and that evolved and changed very quickly. The widely distributed animals are most likely to appear today as fossils in many different places, and a short-lived species allows scientists to date rocks to within, say, tens and not thousands of millions of years. The ammonites – octopus-like animals with coiled shells – are very good for

dating Mesozoic rocks (between 65 and 250 million years ago), since they floated in all the seas of the world in that period. Early Paleozoic rocks (400–590 million years ago) are usually dated by their graptolites – small animals with skeletons consisting of a row of cups along a branch. When these creatures died they sank to the bottom of the sea, so they are found in all kinds of marine sediments like shale and limestone. Ammonites and graptolites are just two examples of what geologists call index fossils.

ENVIRONMENTAL INDICATORS
Some animals only lived on particular kinds of sediments and in certain conditions. When geologists find the fossils of these creatures they can tell what the environment was like when the rock was formed. For example, certain present-day shellfish only live in mud that has no oxygen. Their distant ancestors probably thrived in identical conditions.

Oil geologists find this information very useful, because they know the conditions under which oil-bearing rocks formed, and are looking for rocks that contain such fossils. These specimens are called facies fossils.

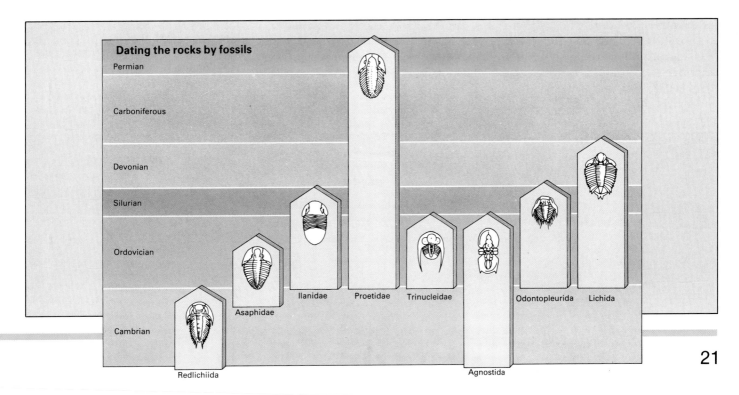

Dating the rocks by fossils

Permian

Carboniferous

Devonian

Silurian

Ordovician

Cambrian

Redlichiida

Asaphidae

Ilanidae

Proetidae

Trinucleidae

Agnostida

Odontopleurida

Lichida

THE ORIGINS OF LIFE

From a submersible, a scientist lowers a camera to the deepest, coldest, darkest abyss of the ocean and photographs a wriggling worm. Life! It pervades every corner of the Earth. But from where did the first living things come? How did life begin?

The origin of life is one of science's greatest mysteries. Over the years many people have put forward different theories and ideas on the subject, but few of these can be tested scientifically. There is as yet no way of devising an experiment and creating life anew in a laboratory. At present all we can do is look at what little evidence we have and speculate on what may have happened on the Earth's surface soon after it formed 4,600 million years ago.

MAKE-UP OF LIVING THINGS

Going back through the complicated picture of animal life, from the most complex to the most primitive, we pass from the creatures made up of many structures or organs, such as lions and whales, through those that are only made of an aggregate of cells, for example the pond creature *Hydra*, to those that consist of a single cell, like bacteria. Yet there are more primitive living things, more simple than a cell. The best examples are viruses. Each virus consists of little more than a long molecule (of the genetic material deoxyribonucleic acid, DNA, or ribonucleic acid, RNA) that has the power to reproduce itself from the substance of any living thing that it invades. It does this by taking over the victim's cell machinery then using the chemicals that surround it and matching them up to its own chemical structure.

So now we can think of the simplest living thing not as a cell but as some sort of a molecule that has the ability to absorb chemicals from its environment and reproduce itself.

A CHEMICAL ORIGIN

The most basic chemicals of living things (biochemicals) are proteins and nucleic acids. These are large complex molecules of mainly carbon, hydrogen, nitrogen and oxygen atoms (in chemistry denoted as C, H, N and O). Each protein is made up of smaller units called amino acids and each nucleic acid of nucleotides.

It may be impossible to create life in the laboratory, but it is possible to create amino acids and nucleotides. If an electric current is passed through a sealed flask containing water (H_2O) and a mixture of the gases carbon monoxide (CO), ammonia (NH_3) and hydrogen (H_2), the water soon becomes discolored with amino acids made up from the chemicals in the mixture. This mix of gases is the same as the Earth's first atmosphere. It seems likely that the first amino acids formed in the early oceans, when lightning burst through the atmosphere and caused chemical changes in the constituent gases.

IN ON A COMET

There is, however, an alternative explanation. Comets, which are balls of cosmic gas, dust and ice that drift about the solar system in long ellipse-shaped orbits, contain the identical chemicals that are likely to produce amino acids and nucleotides. It is possible that such molecules already exist inside comets, and these were spread through the early oceans when comets collided with the young Earth.

Wherever the first amino acids, and nucleotides came from, their existence still does not answer how life started. There is a property of two types of nucleotide molecules, DNA and RNA, that gives them the ability to reproduce. If either of these change themselves so that this ability is enhanced, then all the subsequently reproduced molecules will have the change. A new type of molecule, with different properties, will have arisen. Evolution will have begun.

▼Life's timescale shows an increase in the appearance of new types of creatures as time progresses. Life on Earth probably began about 3,500 million years ago. For most of the early eras life forms were simple, being no more complex than single cells. There is no evidence for multicelled animals or plants until 750 million years ago.

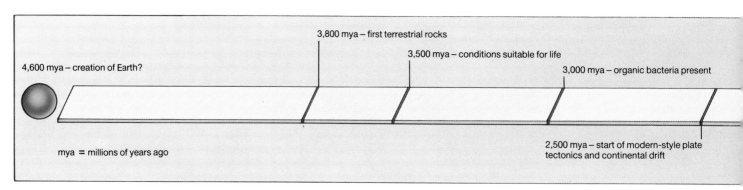

4,600 mya – creation of Earth?

3,800 mya – first terrestrial rocks

3,500 mya – conditions suitable for life

3,000 mya – organic bacteria present

2,500 mya – start of modern-style plate tectonics and continental drift

mya = millions of years ago

▲The most famous experiment on the origin of life was conducted by Stanley Miller in the United States in the 1950s. He took a glass vessel containing a wet mixture of gases like those in the Earth's early atmosphere and passed an electric spark through it to simulate lightning. The carbon, hydrogen, oxygen and nitrogen in the gases united to produce the kinds of chemicals that make up living things.

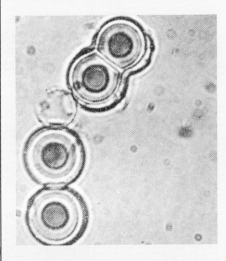

◄An idea popular in the 1920s was that the first living thing was a simple cell. Experiments in the 1970s seem to point in this direction too. Scientists heated organic chemicals until they melted, and then cooled them quickly. They formed microscopic spheres, sometimes linked together, that appeared to have the structure of primitive cells.

▲Today, living things exist in the most hostile of environments. In the hot, chemical-rich waters of volcanic hot springs, there are certain kinds of bacteria that thrive. It is reasonable to suggest that similar living things existed in the harsh environments of the surface of the young Earth many millions of years ago.

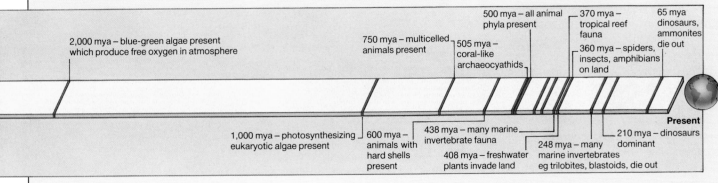

2,000 mya – blue-green algae present which produce free oxygen in atmosphere

750 mya – multicelled animals present

505 mya – coral-like archaeocyathids

500 mya – all animal phyla present

370 mya – tropical reef fauna

360 mya – spiders, insects, amphibians on land

65 mya dinosaurs, ammonites die out

1,000 mya – photosynthesizing eukaryotic algae present

600 mya – animals with hard shells present

438 mya – many marine invertebrate fauna

408 mya – freshwater plants invade land

248 mya – many marine invertebrates eg trilobites, blastoids, die out

210 mya – dinosaurs dominant

Present

ADAPTATION OF SPECIES

A little bird hops along the ground, pecking at fallen seeds with its thick beak. Above it, on a branch, another bird with a smaller beak uses a cactus thorn to winkle a grub from its woody tunnel. Among the twigs at the branch tip a third bird, with a long narrow bill, chases small insects that flit about the flowers. All these species of bird have evolved from a single ancestor within the last 4 million years.

An animal, for instance a wolf, gives birth to a litter of puppies (cubs). The youngsters are all essentially identical to their parents, but two are slightly different. One has shorter legs than its litter-mates while the other has longer legs. The one with shorter legs cannot run as fast as its brothers and sisters. It cannot catch enough food and it soon dies. The puppy with longer legs can run faster. It can catch birds while the others catch only rabbits. It survives and thrives. If it breeds, its offspring may or may not have the longer legs. If they do, a whole line of long-legged wolves is established. As adults, these wolves may prefer to mate with other long-legged individuals. Eventually, two separate populations of wolves develop, one with short legs, one with long legs. This is evolution.

STASIS OR CHANGE?

In big populations of animals these changes tend to go unnoticed. Most individuals are of the "normal" type and, as adults, they breed and produce normal offspring. If a normal wolf breeds with a long-legged wolf, then the offspring will usually be normal. It is in small populations, as in a group of animals marooned on an island, that the changes are more obvious and have a marked effect. Once the "abnormal" body feature develops, it will arise again and again

The five-toed plan

Animals and plants gradually change and adapt to different environments, enabling them to live in new conditions as they develop. Biologists call this process adaptive radiation, since all the subsequent types of populations can be seen to be spreading out, or radiating, from a basic model. The same is true of the anatomical parts of animals and plants. The basic plan of a vertebrate's (backboned animal's) limb is shown here. A single bone supports a pair of bones, which in turn support five rows of smaller bones. The first bone forms the upper arm or the upper leg. The second two bones are the bones of the forearm or the lower leg. The five rows of smaller bones comprise the hand and fingers or the foot and toes.

All the varied limbs of vertebrate animals can be seen as an adaptation of this basic "pentadactyl" (from the Greek meaning five-digit) pattern. Few creatures have retained this pattern unaltered. A limb used for walking or flying needs a different arrangement of bones from a limb used for swimming.

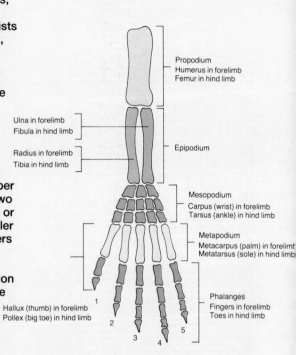

Primitive "phalangeal formula" 2:3:4:5:4

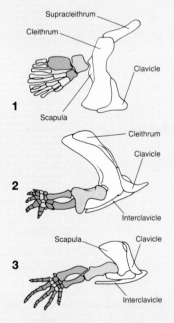

►The fins of the ancestral lobe-finned fish, like those of the modern catfish, enabled it to crawl on land.

◄**From water to land** The ancestors of today's land-living vertebrates were the lobe-finned fish. These had chunky fins supported by a network of bone (1). The bones in the base of the limb are still present in the descendants, the amphibian (2) and the reptile (3) limbs, but the disorganized outer elements have evolved into toes.

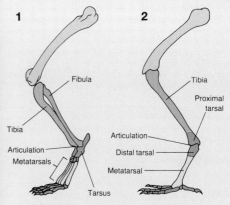

1

Fibula

2

Tibia

Proximal tarsal

Tibia

Articulation

Articulation

Distal tarsal

Metatarsals

Metatarsal

Tarsus

◀▲**Walking on tiptoes** Most mammals and birds walk on their toes – the "digitigrade" condition. This means that the long foot bones can be used as part of the leg. In running mammals, like the Maned wolf (left), all the muscles are concentrated at the top of the leg (**1**), making the rest of the leg lightweight for fast movement. In a bird's leg (**2**), many of the bones, including one of the lower leg bones and most of the long foot bones have been lost. This helps to keep down the weight for flight.

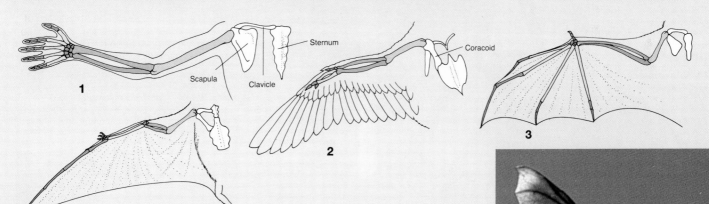

Sternum

Scapula

Clavicle

1

Coracoid

2

3

4

▲▶**Like and unlike** Many animals have developed wings, but in different groups they have evolved in varying ways. The human arm (**1**) can be used as the basic plan. In a bird's wing (**2**), all the muscles are attached to the upper and lower arm. Nearly all the hand bones and finger bones have been lost. The bat's wing (**3 and right**) is a web of skin supported by an outspread hand of narrow fingers. Each finger consists mostly of the long bones making up the palm of the human hand. The pterosaur, an ancient flying reptile, had a wing (**4**) that consisted of a web of skin supported by a very long and strong fourth finger. In the most advanced species, the hand bones were also long.

because there are not enough normal individuals to dilute its effect. In small areas the choice of food is limited. Only if the animals change and the change turns out to help them to exploit the food, can they survive. So new species develop most quickly on islands and in areas where populations of animals cannot easily mix.

UP TO 30 MILLION SPECIES

As different environments develop, each with unique living conditions and a variety of types of food, new animals quickly evolve to live there and take advantage of the new opportunities. When a new food source becomes available, creatures will evolve to eat it. With so many different kinds of food around in the world today, it is not surprising that so many different species of animal (at least 1,250,000) have developed.

TWO-HANDS HIGH

The process of change has happened throughout time. Early in the Tertiary period, about 50 or 60 million years ago, there were tropical forests in most areas of the world. The dinosaurs had quite recently become extinct, and the mammals had evolved into all shapes and sizes to fill the vacant habitats and environments. One of these early mammals was the ancestor of the modern horse.

Hyracotherium was only about the size of a rabbit and went scampering through the forest undergrowth nibbling leaves. A few million years later the forests began to thin and a larger and swifter horse evolved. This was still only 26in high at the shoulder.

In the Miocene period, about 25 million years ago, the forests gave way to grasslands. With drier climates, open prairies and savannahs spread over the continents. The different types of horse evolved to meet the new conditions.

GRASS-EATERS

Grass is a very tough substance to eat, and so the jaws of the Miocene horses became powerful and the teeth tall-crowned and very hard. Crinkled enamel, which developed as covering on the teeth, produced a grinding surface that could tear apart the fibrous grass leaves. On the open grassland there is nowhere to hide, but animals can see danger coming from a long way off. For an animal that may fall victim to a predator, its only means of escape is to run away. The early grassland horses developed long necks, allowing them to survey the landscape, and long faces so that their eyes were still above the grass while their muzzles were at the ground chewing. Long running legs soon developed, worked by tendons powered by muscles concentrated at the top of the limbs. The toes got smaller to make the feet lightweight, so that eventually only one toe on each foot, armed with a strong hoof, remained. Gradually, a horse evolved that resembled the modern version.

►The modern genus *Equus*, which includes the horses, such as these Iceland ponies, and zebras, is the only survivor of a very varied and long evolutionary series.

◄▼The history of the horse Many early members branched off to different environments and became extinct (right). The earliest was *Hyracotherium* (1), which fed in the undergrowth. It had a weak jaw, low-crowned teeth and four toes on its fore-feet. It was succeeded by the larger *Mesohippus* (2). Then, when the grasslands arrived, *Merychippus* (3) and other early grass-eaters evolved. By *Pliohippus* (4) the teeth and jaws had become strong and there was only one toe on each foot. It began to look like modern *Equus* (5).

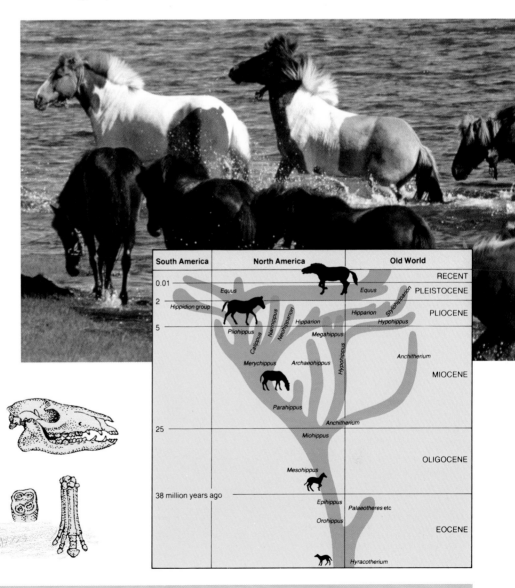

THE SHAPE OF EVOLUTION

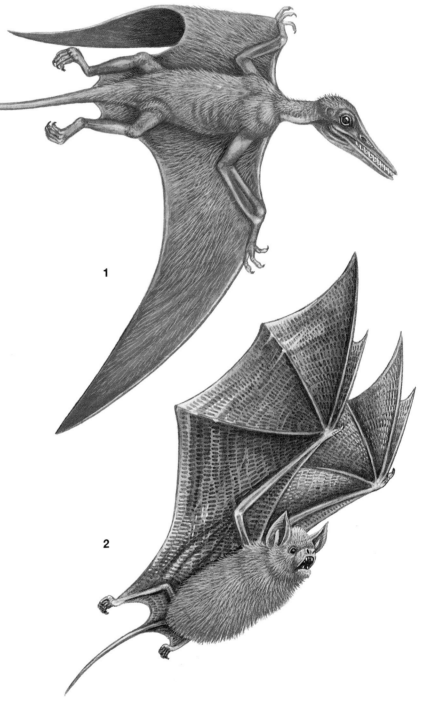

Insects swirl and gyrate in a shaft of sunlight between the trees. They are disturbed. A flying squirrel glides by and lands on a branch. The squirrel is no threat to the insects, unlike the swallow that next appears and the bats that will come out at dusk. These various flying creatures, each with a unique type of wing, have evolved in different ways.

The process of evolution known as adaptive radiation involves one type of creature changing into different forms, each adapted to the particular environment in which it lives. There is another process, called convergence, that produces the opposite, namely various creatures independently acquire very similar characteristics in response to similar changes in their environments.

EARLY FLIGHT

An example of convergent evolution is the history of flight among animals. As soon as animal life emerged from the water over 400 million years ago, certain creatures left the land and took to the skies. Insects were among the first land animals, and they were also the first to fly.

Near the beginning of the Age of Reptiles, in Permian and Triassic times – 213 to 286 million years ago – there were reptiles that could glide through the air. They were all like lizards with wings, supported by extended ribs, which provided their bodies with lift. Then true flying reptiles, the pterosaurs, evolved. These had wings that were attached to their forelimbs and elongated fourth fingers. Their bones and muscles show that they could flap their wings and did not just glide.

At the same time that the pterosaurs were masters of the air, birds evolved, and these have remained the dominant flyers to this day.

▲**Flying reptiles and mammals**
Different flying animals evolved different designs of wing. The flying reptiles, or pterosaurs such as *Rhamphorhynchus* (1), had wings that consisted of broad membranes attached to the forelimbs and very long fourth fingers. The earliest bat, *Icaronycteris* (2), had wings like a modern bat, supported on outstretched hands.

Finally, with the extinction of the great reptiles and the coming of the mammals, several flying mammals developed. Some, like flying squirrels, were gliders but the true mammalian fliers were the bats.

THE MECHANICS OF FLIGHT

What did all these creatures have in common? Their flying life-style meant that they needed some kind of special structure, musculature and skeleton that would allow them to take off from the ground, maintain lift, and land. So each needed a type of wing.

A wing must have certain basic properties. It must be broad and flat, to catch the air. It must be shaped so that air passing over and under it provides lift, or at least the air spills out slowly to give buoyancy and to slow a fall. The wing must be light-weight in order to be easy to move and not make the animal too heavy or cumbersome. All these problems have been solved, not once, but many times in the course of evolution. As a result, many different creatures have wings, and the structure and functioning of these varies considerably.

ADAPTED FOR SWIMMING

What is true of flight, is true of all other ways of life. A swimming life-style places similarly strict conditions on any creature that takes it up. To push through the water with least resistance an animal needs to have a smooth streamlined surface. It needs paddles or fins to provide the propulsion. It needs stabilizing surfaces to allow it to control its position in the water.

Again, all these problems have been solved in a number of different ways by a variety of creatures. Fish are the most common and widespread of large swimming creatures. They have a smooth torpedo-like shape, with a broad tail fin to provide propulsion and an arrangement of other fins to control the stability in the water. During the Age of Reptiles, reptile groups, such as the plesiosaurs and ichthyosaurs, returned to the sea which had spawned their ancestors. They adopted a streamlined shape, tail fins and stabilizing flippers. Once they died out, their places were taken by early types of whales and dolphins. These resembled the aquatic reptiles, yet they were mammals just like lions, monkeys and humans. Another case of convergence.

◀▲ **Flying birds and insects** The earliest known bird, *Archaeopteryx* (1), had the same arrangement of wing feathers as a modern bird, although the limbs themselves were very primitive and reptile-like. Insects, such as the ancient giant dragonfly *Meganeura* (2), have always had two pairs of wings made from the tough horny substance, chitin, which covers insect bodies and legs.

29

Convergence, or convergent evolution, does not just work on individual organs such as wings or fins. It works on entire animals and plants. It is as if a particular environment or life-style imposes a particular shape on any animal that lives there or behaves in that manner, and this shape crops up time and again throughout evolutionary history.

MANY MEAT-EATERS
The meat-eating mammals are a case in point. Most present-day meat-eating mammals are grouped together in the taxonomic class Carnivora. They are usually called the carnivores. They include the weasels, the dogs, the cats and the bears. In the early Tertiary period, the carnivores as a group were not very common or widespread. Instead, the main meat-eating mammals were a group of beasts called the creodonts. If we could look at these, we would think that the creodonts were conventional carnivores. There were some small creodonts that chased other small mammals down long burrows and through the undergrowth. These looked like modern weasels. There were larger creodonts that stalked and ambushed larger prey. They all resembled today's wild cats and dogs.

When the creodonts all died out in the mid-Tertiary, about 25 million years ago, the carnivores evolved to take their places and developed the same shapes.

RECENT CONVERGENCE
Convergence can also produce the same shapes in different groups of animals at the same time.

It is often difficult to tell seals and sea lions apart because they both have the same streamlined shape and identical swimming paddles. Yet the seals evolved from the group of carnivores that produced the otters, while sea lions evolved from the group that gave rise to the dogs. The same structure and form evolved independently.

Other classic examples are found in Australia. This vast continent has been isolated from all the others for more than 50 million years, and evolution

has been allowed to go its own way there. As a result, the native pouched-mammals, the marsupials, evolved to live in all the environments of the continent. By convergence, they evolved the same body shapes that developed among the other mammals in similar environments in other parts of the world such as South America.

▼ ► **Examples of convergent evolution** Australian marsupial mammals look just like the placental mammals of the rest of the world that have the same life-styles. The meat-eating thylacine (**1a**) has the dog-like face and the running paws of the wolf (**1b**). The quoll (**2a**) hunts birds and small mammals as does the ocelot (**2b**). The mulgara (**3a**) and wood mouse (**3b**). The marsupial glider (**4a**) and the flying squirrel (**4b**). The numbat (**5a**) and Giant anteater (**5b**). The Marsupial and Californian moles (**6a, 6b**). These animals are all unrelated.

ISOLATION AND SPECIES

A fearsome-looking creature hauls itself out of the sea on to a rock. It has a block-shaped head covered with horns and knobs, black scaly skin, long curved claws, and a powerful tail with a jagged crest. This is no primitive throwback to the Age of Dinosaurs but a quite new species. The Marine iguana of the Galapagos islands has only evolved since the islands appeared out of the water 4 million years ago.

A species such as the Marine iguana is defined as a group of creatures that are capable of breeding with one another and the offspring of such breedings are fertile. Taking another example, a carthorse can breed with a racehorse and their offspring, a foal, will itself be able to breed (with other foals) when it becomes adult. This is because the carthorse and racehorse are of the same species, *Equus caballus*. However, if a racehorse and a donkey breed, they will produce a foal, called a mule, which will not be fertile. The donkey is a different species, *Equus asinus*.

Large populations of a species do not change in character very much over long periods of time. With great numbers of individuals breeding with one another, any tendency for the average appearance and behavior of the population to change will be diluted. It is when small groups of animals happen to split away from the main population that change and evolution occurs quite rapidly.

EVOLUTION'S LABORATORY

Islands are perfect locations for evolution, and the volcanic Galapagos islands in the Pacific Ocean off Ecuador are perhaps the best-known examples. Iguana lizards from the mainland colonized the islands soon after their formation 4 million years ago. The animals were probably carried there on tree trunks washed out to sea. Conditions on the islands were so unlike those on the mainland that only those iguanas that were able to change and adapt to the new environment survived. They adopted a diet of seaweeds, and took up a swimming mode of life – the only lizards in the world to do so. Now their successors, the Marine iguanas, are very different from their tree-living, meat-eating relatives on the mainland. They would not possibly be able to interbreed. They have become a new species.

Also on the Galapagos islands are many different species of finch, made famous by the studies of Charles Darwin. Each species exploits a different food supply. The finches would all have evolved from a single species blown over from the South American mainland. Those that developed ground-feeding habits would have kept themselves apart from those with treetop-feeding habits and so on.

WATCH THE CHANGES

A change in characteristics of an animal that forms the basis of evolution is rarely seen. The story of the Peppered moth is perhaps the closest that scientists have come to recording evolution in action.

The Peppered moth, a species widespread in Europe, comes in two different color schemes – the typical light phase and a dark phase. The light phase is normally well-camouflaged against tree bark and survives while birds pick off its more conspicuous dark cousins. During the Industrial Revolution that swept 19th-century England, tree trunks became black with soot. The dark phase was then camouflaged and the light phase began to be killed off. The new environment had imposed strong selection within the species. With the coming of clean-air laws in the mid-20th century, the amount of clean tree

▼▶ Against a clean tree trunk (below), the light-colored form of the Peppered moth is camouflaged. The dark form is easily seen and is eaten by birds. Against a sooty trunk (right), it is the dark form that is camouflaged and survives.

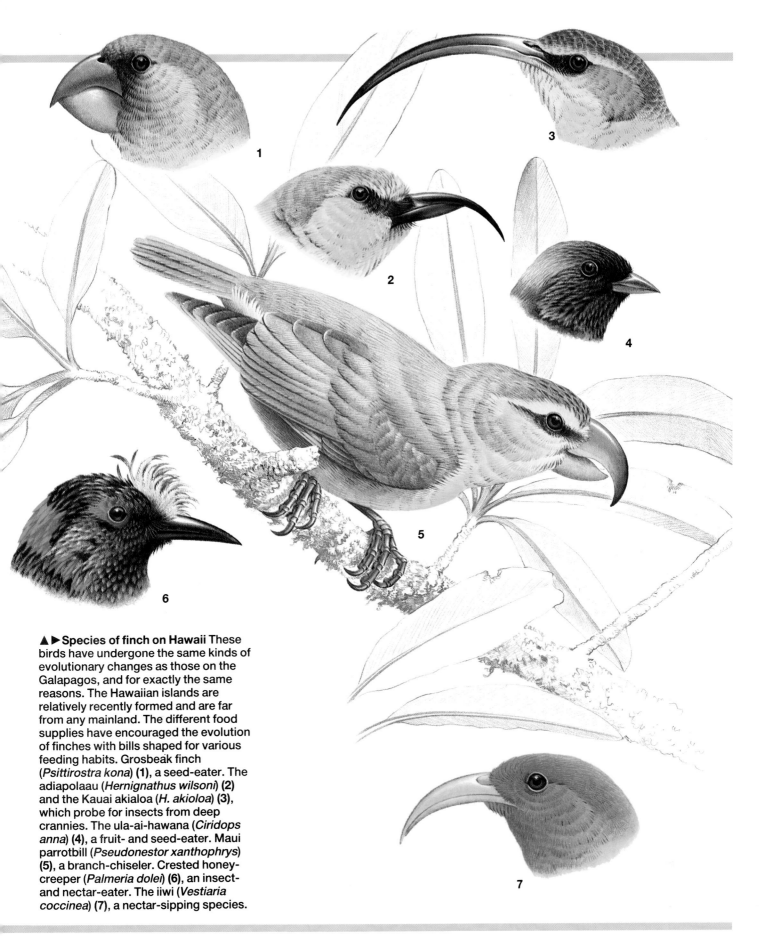

▲ ▶ **Species of finch on Hawaii** These birds have undergone the same kinds of evolutionary changes as those on the Galapagos, and for exactly the same reasons. The Hawaiian islands are relatively recently formed and are far from any mainland. The different food supplies have encouraged the evolution of finches with bills shaped for various feeding habits. Grosbeak finch (*Psittirostra kona*) **(1)**, a seed-eater. The adiapolaau (*Hernignathus wilsoni*) **(2)** and the Kauai akialoa (*H. akioloa*) **(3)**, which probe for insects from deep crannies. The ula-ai-hawana (*Ciridops anna*) **(4)**, a fruit- and seed-eater. Maui parrotbill (*Pseudonestor xanthophrys*) **(5)**, a branch-chiseler. Crested honey-creeper (*Palmeria dolei*) **(6)**, an insect- and nectar-eater. The iiwi (*Vestiaria coccinea*) **(7)**, a nectar-sipping species.

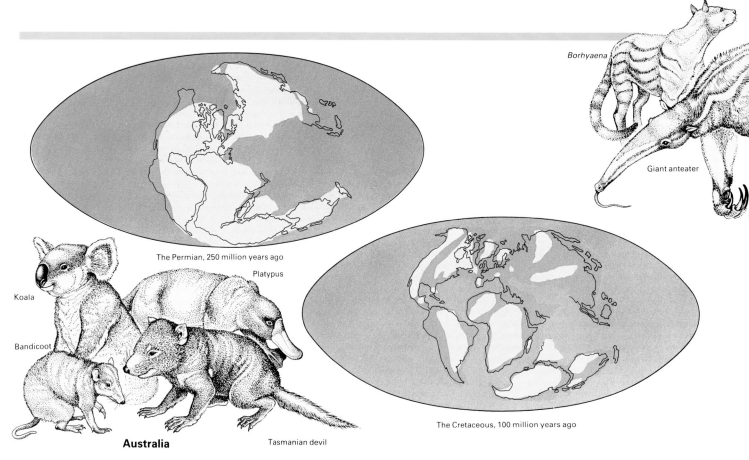

Borhyaena

Giant anteater

Koala

Platypus

Bandicoot

The Permian, 250 million years ago

The Cretaceous, 100 million years ago

Australia

Tasmanian devil

bark increased. Populations of the light-colored moth flourished again while those of the dark-colored form dwindled.

THE GEOGRAPHY OF ANIMALS
Just as islands tend to have different animals (and plants) from their mainlands, so the different continents of the world have their own unique collection of creatures.

The main reason for the distribution of animal life that we see today is the history of the movements of the Earth's land masses. Between the late Permian and the middle Jurassic periods – from about 250 to 160 million years ago – all the continents of the world were jammed together and formed a single giant land mass. Geologists call this supercontinent Pangaea.

The dinosaurs lived on this supercontinent, as did the early mammals. During the late Jurassic period, about 150 million years ago, Pangaea began to split apart into the continents that

exist today. Each of them carried a selection of the animals that lived on the supercontinent.

UNUSUAL AUSTRALIAN LIFE
At first, the most widespread of the mammals were the pouched species, the marsupials. They were particularly well established in Australia and South America. In other parts of the world, in the Tertiary period, these gave way to the placental mammals. Australia had no placental species, except for a few bats, and to the present-day the marsupials are the most important mammals there.

Over the past 50 million years the continent of Australia has broken free from Antarctica and moved northwards. Now it straddles the Tropic of Capricorn. The marsupials were evolving all this time to keep pace with the changing conditions. Also on Australia there are two representatives of the very primitive egg-laying mammals, the monotremes, and these are not found anywhere else in the world.

▲The break-up of the supercontinent Pangaea led to the the original mammal fauna becoming dispersed around the world. Once the continents were separated, evolution could work at its own rate on the different land masses.

ONE-WAY TRAFFIC
South America had not only a large number of marsupials, but also many primitive species of placental mammals. The placentals developed into plant-eating animals that resembled modern camels and hippopotamuses, while the marsupials became wolf-like and tiger-like carnivores. This was a result of convergent evolution.

Evolution was slow on South America as climatic conditions did not change very quickly. Large animals, for example, the Giant ground sloth, evolved in the late Tertiary period. Then, a land-bridge was thrown up between North America and South America. This was the land mass that formed today's Central America. Modern-type placental mammals flooded southwards from the north

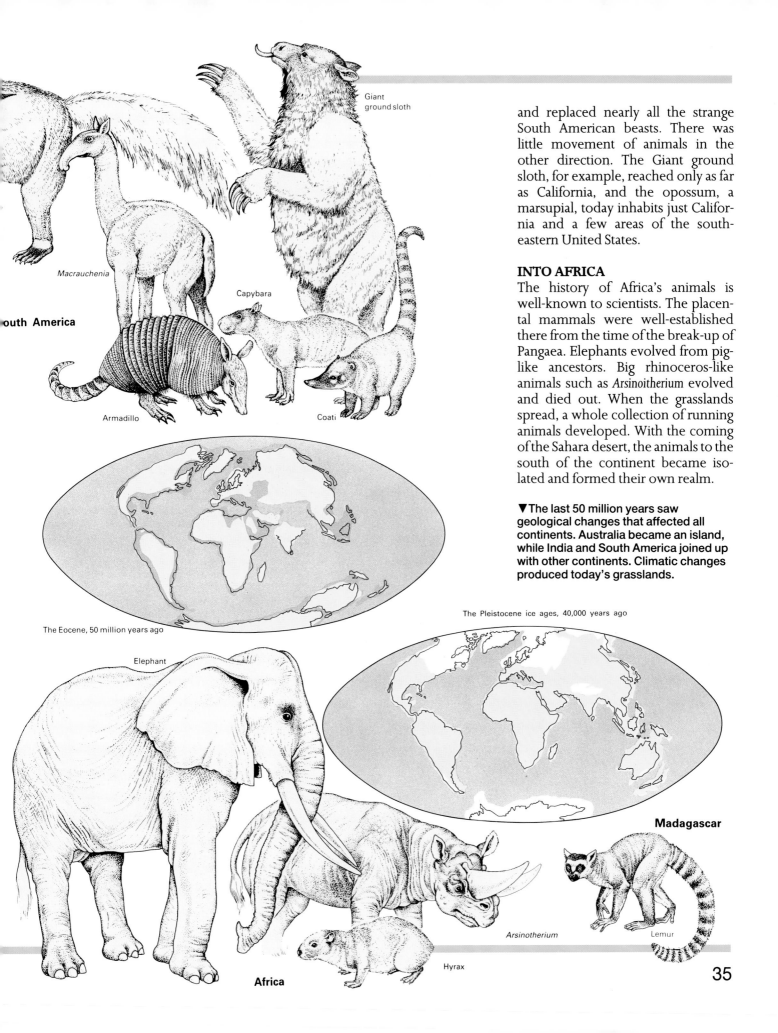

Giant
ground sloth

Macrauchenia

South America

Capybara

Armadillo

Coati

The Eocene, 50 million years ago

and replaced nearly all the strange South American beasts. There was little movement of animals in the other direction. The Giant ground sloth, for example, reached only as far as California, and the opossum, a marsupial, today inhabits just California and a few areas of the south-eastern United States.

INTO AFRICA

The history of Africa's animals is well-known to scientists. The placental mammals were well-established there from the time of the break-up of Pangaea. Elephants evolved from pig-like ancestors. Big rhinoceros-like animals such as *Arsinoitherium* evolved and died out. When the grasslands spread, a whole collection of running animals developed. With the coming of the Sahara desert, the animals to the south of the continent became isolated and formed their own realm.

▼The last 50 million years saw geological changes that affected all continents. Australia became an island, while India and South America joined up with other continents. Climatic changes produced today's grasslands.

The Pleistocene ice ages, 40,000 years ago

Elephant

Madagascar

Arsinotherium

Lemur

Hyrax

Africa

35

DOMESTICATION

The farmer pats his dog and goes out to do a late evening check on his animals. In the hen coop the chickens snuggle down for the night. In the barn the cows lazily chew the cud, turning grass into milk. Over in the sty the enormous pigs, heavy with meat for the market, waddle with an unnatural gait.

As the human species developed, the first societies were "hunter-gatherers." Their members went out to hunt whatever wild animals they could find, and to gather fruits, seeds and edible plants from the wilderness round about.

True civilization developed when early peoples found that life was easier if, instead of hunting wildlife, they caught animals such as wild pigs, cattle, goats and sheep and penned them up and looked after them until they were needed. It was also preferable to remove plants from the wilderness and to grow them in easily tended plots close to home. This change of behavior, about 10,000 years ago, marked the development of farming. Animals were domesticated – tamed to live with people – and plants cultivated – grown, looked after and produced as crops.

CHANGING THE ANIMALS

Early farmers soon found that if they could induce the pigs with most meat or the cows that gave most milk to mate, they could rear offspring that themselves would give more meat or milk. The practice was pursued through the history of farming and continues today. The result is a whole range of domesticated animals, all bred for different purposes and looking different from one another.

This process of "selective breeding" can be regarded as a kind of applied evolution. The animals themselves provide whatever change in characteristics occurs, but the farmer and breeder decide which changes are beneficial and should be sustained.

In the future, it may be possible to control the changes themselves, using genetic engineering. Scientists can already alter the genetic make-up, the hereditary blueprint, of organisms such as bacteria.

NEW SHAPES

Food animals were bred to give more food. The result was bigger pigs with lots more meat, or cows producing more milk than normal for the amount of grass eaten or hens laying a greater number of eggs. Few of the modern breeds of livestock would be able to survive in the wild. They have been so highly bred that they need the artificial environments and care provided by farmers.

Early civilizations realized that in addition to providing food, some large animals could be exploited for their strength and used for transport. Horses, asses, camels, llamas and yaks were all used as pack animals and horses and bullocks (castrated bulls) as draft animals to pull plows and carts. They were all bred for greater

▼**Physical changes associated with domestication** The Lop (1) is a floppy-eared form of the European Wild rabbit (2). Most pet dogs are smaller than their wolf ancestors (3) and their coats usually provide less camouflage. The Pug (4), a Toy dog bred for show and as a household companion, has a shorter face, a more rounded head and modified ears and tail.

strength or speed. Some of these animals, along with sheep and goats, were bred for their hides or wool.

VOLUNTARY DOMESTICATION
A few species came to be domesticated seemingly by choice. When grain is stored, rats and mice come to steal it to eat. Cats soon learned about this and came in from the wild to hunt the rats and mice. They were tolerated by the early farmers because they kept down the pests.

Dogs also gathered round the early settlements, feeding on scraps and left-overs. It was soon realized how useful they were, and farmers bred them for hunting and later for controlling flocks of sheep. Their present role as pets came much later.

▲Formerly domesticated animals that now live wild, like these mustangs in Wyoming, USA, are called feral.

▲Wild and domesticated sheep, pigs and cattle From the wild mouflon (1), sheep varieties such as the Jacob (2) and Tasmanian Merino (3) have been bred. The Wild boar (4) is much larger and stronger than the Pot-bellied pig (5). The wild aurochs (6) has large horns, the domesticated Shorthorn (7) small ones.

PRECAMBRIAN LIFE

Harsh sunlight slants through the murk and poison of the primitive atmosphere and glistens on the oily surface of the warm ocean. Below the undulating surface a drifting jelly-like mass stains the water. It is a cloud of tiny particles, each of which is a living, reproducing cell. The cells have the potential for evolving into all the kinds of creatures that are to inherit the Earth.

Scientists do not know exactly where life came from, but they are reasonably sure that conditions on Earth were suitable for some form of life 3,500 million years ago. If we knew precisely when life first appeared, we could put a date on the first major point of geological time, the boundary between the Archean and the Proterozoic eras. These are the two major divisions of that vast sweep of time, from about 4,600 to 590 million years ago, called the Precambrian.

The Archean era is defined as that period of time during which no life existed. During the Proterozoic era some form of life was present, even if just a few self-replicating molecules. The Proterozoic lasted up to about 590 million years ago, the beginning of the Cambrian period, when animals with hard shells first evolved.

THE TEEMING MOLECULES

Scientists surmise that the first living things were merely complex molecules that had the power to copy (reproduce, replicate) themselves. They would have lived in water that was full of carbon-rich chemical substances such as amino acids, the building blocks from which proteins are made. This rich mixture is often referred to as the primordial soup.

Each replicating molecule would have been a long chain of atoms, and would have reproduced itself by allowing molecules from the liquid all around to gather along its length, matching up atom for atom with the original structure. When this was complete, the two molecules would split apart, and each part would have its own life. This could only go on if there were enough amino acids and other raw materials floating about in the primordial soup. Sooner or later these would become used up – all turned into self-replicating molecules.

The next stage of evolution would have come when one molecule developed the ability to absorb another, already existing, molecule. It

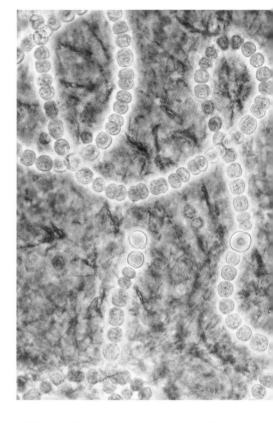

▲ Modern blue-green algae are primitive plant-like organisms consisting of long strings of individual simple cells.

would then turn the substance of this molecule into raw material that it could use for itself. It was the first hunter – a precursor animal, perhaps.

The energy of the Sun would have been used next. This would have been harnessed by some molecules and used to build up the raw materials from very simple chemicals in the water. We could regard these molecules as the first plants. By this time there would have been many different types of micro-organisms, some generating food, others feeding from one another and a third type scavenging the remains of their counterparts.

THE FIRST CELLS

Rocks containing tiny structures that look like bacteria have been found in strata that are 3,000 million years old. The next recognizable remains of

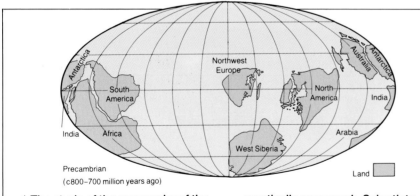

▲ The study of the geography of the ancient Earth – paleogeography – becomes less and less precise the further back in time we look. Precambrian paleogeography is practically guesswork. Scientists know that continental masses existed at least 3,900 million years ago, but these would have been in different positions from today's continents.

Precambrian
(c800–700 million years ago)

Land

primitive organisms all date from about 2,000 million years ago. These appear to be blue-green algae. This is understandable when we look at the life-styles and characteristics of some modern micro-organisms. A bacterium is the simplest form of cell known to scientists today. The next simplest is that of a blue-green alga. Such an algal cell has a much more complicated structure, but it still lacks the cell nucleus. This is the clump of protein and genetic material at the heart of "advanced" cells typically those of plants and animals, which controls the cells' workings.

Modern blue-green algae exist as strings of cells, and these often lie on shallow sea floors as sticky mats. As tides and currents wash mud over these, some of the mud particles stick to the surface of the mats. More strands of algae grow on top of this layer of mud, and these trap a new covering of particles. This goes on until hummocks of algal mats and muddy layers grow up on the sea bed. These are called stromatolites and they are usually about the size of garbage can lids.

Stromatolites are rare and only form where there are no burrowing or surface-feeding animals to disturb their formation. The blue-green algae remains of 2,000 million years ago consist of rock structures that have been interpreted as fossils of these stromatolites.

LIFE AS WE KNOW IT

The first single-celled green algae – the most primitive types of cell that have a conventional nucleus – lived about 1,300 million years ago. Fossils of these cells have been found preserved in chert, a fine-grained silica rock from younger Precambrian rocks.

The chemical reactions that support life inside a blue-green alga cell and a green cell are similar to those that support life in any plant. The energy of sunlight is used to build up food from the surrounding water together with carbon dioxide and other gases in the atmosphere. The process is known as photosynthesis, and this produces oxygen as a by-product. In Precambrian times the Earth's oceans became saturated with dissolved oxygen, and free oxygen began to build up in the atmosphere – something that had been totally lacking before.

Eventually, conditions on Earth were right for the evolution of other types of biochemical processes, especially those that involved oxygen. In time, animals cells – ones with a nucleus and, using oxygen, breaking down complex molecules to release chemical energy – would develop.

▶Ancient Precambrian structures such as these have been interpreted as fossil stromatolites.

▼Modern stromatolites are dome-shaped masses of mud layers collected by mats of blue-green algae.

MULTI-CELLED CREATURES

Once complex cells had evolved, evolution proceeded apace. Single cells at first gave rise to groups or colonies of individual cells, and then to multi-celled creatures. These consisted of large collections of cells, with each cell having a specific function. The colonies were like the strings of blue-green algae which were just identical cells stuck together. The multi-celled creatures may have evolved by individual cells dividing and then splitting (budding) off from one another and failing to separate completely. Or they evolved when individual free cells came together and lived in close proximity.

Soon the multi-celled creatures became more complex and sophisticated, with clumps of cells growing into different layers and structures, called tissues and organs respectively. Each organ had a particular job to do in keeping the creature alive and ensuring it replicated. At last the true "advanced" organism had evolved.

THE FIRST CLEAR RECORD

The known history of multi-celled organisms dates back to about 700 million years ago.

Rocks dating from before the Cambrian period 590 million years ago are famous for their lack of fossils. In the Flinders and Mount Lofty Ranges in southern Australia there is a sequence of barren rocks, consisting of layer upon layer of limestone, sandstone and mudstone 60ft thick. At the very top, in the youngest beds or strata, there are fossils of Cambrian creatures, showing that the vast bulk of the rock sequence is Precambrian. In the 1940s an Australian geologist, Reg Sprigg, began to look for fossils below the Cambrian bed. After 10 years of searching he came across a bed that contained markings that looked like jellyfish.

So unusual was Sprigg's discovery that it was another decade before the scientific community accepted his findings. The fossils consisted of worms, jellyfish, sea pens (relatives of sea anemones and corals) and all sorts of other marine creatures that it is impossible to identify. The collection of creatures became known as the Ediacara fauna after the Ediacaran Hills where they were discovered.

UNLIKELY EVENTS AND LINKS

In more recent times, a schoolboy found an identical sea pen in Precambrian rocks in Charnwood Forest in central England, and similar fossils have been found in late Precambrian outcrops in Canada, Namibia and northern USSR. It is evident that the animals represented must have lived over a very large area of the globe, probably in every shallow sea. At these localities they must all have fossilized under special circumstances, for example after the gentle deposition of fine material in still water. The remains of soft-bodied creatures do not usually fossilize well.

As well as the fossils of primitive soft-bodied sea creatures, scientists have also found many trace fossils – tracks, trails and burrows in rock. However, it is almost impossible to match up these structures to animals that themselves cannot be clearly identified. All the likely animals seem to have been very flat or very thin, as if they needed a large surface area. Paleontologists now think that this is because the concentration of oxygen in the water at that time was not very high, and each creature needed a big

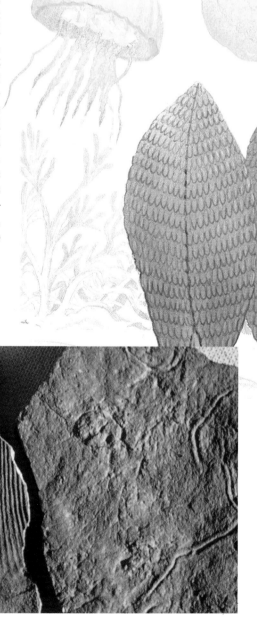

▼Ediacaran fossils consist of the impressions of soft-bodied animals preserved in solidified mud, such as the flatworm *Dickinsonia* (left). There are also trace fossils (right).

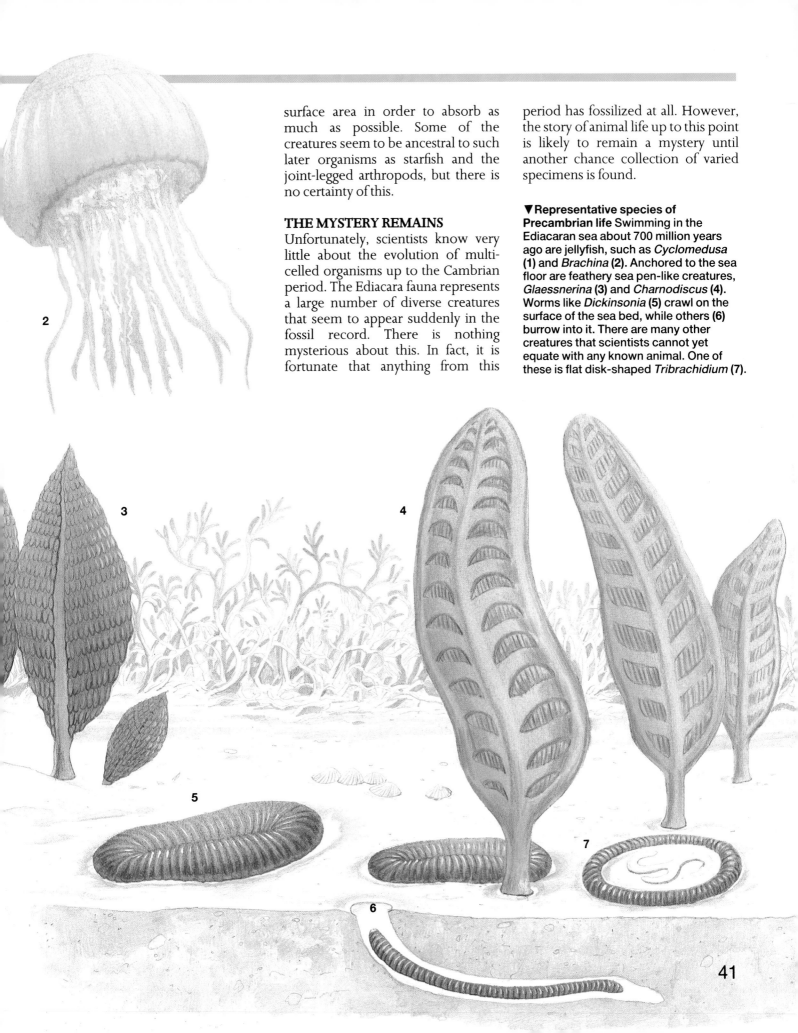

surface area in order to absorb as much as possible. Some of the creatures seem to be ancestral to such later organisms as starfish and the joint-legged arthropods, but there is no certainty of this.

THE MYSTERY REMAINS
Unfortunately, scientists know very little about the evolution of multi-celled organisms up to the Cambrian period. The Ediacara fauna represents a large number of diverse creatures that seem to appear suddenly in the fossil record. There is nothing mysterious about this. In fact, it is fortunate that anything from this period has fossilized at all. However, the story of animal life up to this point is likely to remain a mystery until another chance collection of varied specimens is found.

▼**Representative species of Precambrian life** Swimming in the Ediacaran sea about 700 million years ago are jellyfish, such as *Cyclomedusa* (**1**) and *Brachina* (**2**). Anchored to the sea floor are feathery sea pen-like creatures, *Glaessnerina* (**3**) and *Charnodiscus* (**4**). Worms like *Dickinsonia* (**5**) crawl on the surface of the sea bed, while others (**6**) burrow into it. There are many other creatures that scientists cannot yet equate with any known animal. One of these is flat disk-shaped *Tribrachidium* (**7**).

FOSSIL INVERTEBRATES

On the beach, at the foot of a chalk cliff, a child picks up and studies a chunk of limestone. It is a mass of shells, some whole, others a crushed mess. Segments of sea lily stems lie mixed with shells of coral. When these animals were alive in the sea, 400 million years ago, they formed an impressive reef. She notices that dotted through the rock are the conical shells of the octopus-like animals that swam above the ancient reef.

The vast majority of fossils that people are likely to find in rocks are the remains or impressions of invertebrates – animals that have no backbone or internal skeleton. This is not unexpected. Walk along any beach and you will see millions of sea shells, the remains of invertebrates such as clams, scallops and limpets, but only rarely will you come across the body of a vertebrate (a backboned animal), for instance a fish or dolphin. Invertebrates have always made up the bulk of animals living at any time. This is because they are smaller and therefore need less resources than most vertebrates.

Many types of invertebrate have a hard shell of one sort or another, and it is the hard shells, not the soft parts of the body, that are usually found as fossils. The shells vary in chemical composition.

CALCITE SHELLS
The most common shell material is calcium carbonate, or calcite. The shells people find on the beach are made of this substance. The flesh of the animal secretes the shell using the many chemicals in seawater as raw materials. The shell forms a hard protective cover for all the internal organs such as the heart.

The most prolific group of animals with calcite shells are the molluscs. These include the bivalves that form the typical and most familiar sea shells. First among these are the gastropods, comprising the snails, whelks, winkles and other spirally shelled creatures that crawl on a broad foot. Next are the cephalopods, modern types of which – the octopuses and squids – have no shell, but extinct types like the ammonites did have shells and these are important fossils.

SIMILAR BODY PLANS
The brachiopods are a group of invertebrates that are often confused with the molluscs. They look like bivalves in that each animal is confined between a pair of calcite shells. However, they are in no way related, and the resemblance has come about by convergent evolution; both groups independently adopted the same life-style. The main difference is that whereas a bivalve has a left shell and a right shell which are mirror images of one another, a brachiopod has distinctive top and bottom shells that are very different from each other.

HARD CASES
Many coelenterates also have calcite shells. Coelenterates, such a sea anemones, have a simple sac-like stomach with a mouth surrounded by tentacles. The corals encase this arrangement in a tubular wall of calcite. Modern corals are individually small creatures, but they grow together as huge masses, their combined shells producing reefs. Ancient corals, on the other hand, tended to be larger animals and they lived singly, like armored sea anemones.

Echinoderms comprise the starfish, the sea lilies and the sea urchins. These "spiny-skinned" invertebrates have shells of calcite and are often common as fossils.

CHITIN SHELLS
The second most common shell material is chitin, a horn-like substance containing nitrogen. Fingernails and the claws of carnivores are made of chitin.

The most important chitin-covered animals are the arthropods – animals with jointed legs. Insects are the most obvious examples. However, fossil insects are uncommon compared with the fossils of arthropods that lived in the sea, for example crabs, lobsters and shrimps. During the first half of the Paleozoic era, from 590 to 440 million years ago, there was a very important group of marine arthropods known as the trilobites. These had many centipede-like legs and a

▼ Cephalopods, the animals with tentacles, have been common since 430 million years ago. Most primitive types had a chambered shell that was coiled or straight, as here.

segmented body with a central ridge and a flat area at each side.

Graptolites were small creatures in chitin shells. They are now extinct but are common as early Paleozoic fossils. They were communal creatures, with many individuals growing from a branch and each one encased in a tiny cup. The whole organism was leaf-like and lived either attached to the sea floor or suspended from a jellyfish-like buoyancy bag of gas.

SILICA SHELLS

Sponges have shells of silica – the main constituent of sand – but these are loose groups of tiny needle-like spicules. They usually fall apart after death and it is impossible to see the entire original animal from the shape of the fossil.

Some microscopic creatures called radiolarians have delicate lace-like shells of silica, and these are important as zone fossils (those used to define short time spans) when they are found in the rocks.

▲Looking more like plants than animals, the echinoderm sea lilies grew in thickets on late Paleozoic sea beds. They are more usually found broken up.

▼A complete sea lily fossil shows that the animal resembled a starfish with a stalk anchored to the sea bed.

▲Graptolites consisted of a series of tiny linked individuals. Their communal shells grew as networks of branches. Their fossils are common in deep sea sediments of the Ordovician period, 505 to 438 million years ago. As time went on the number of branches became fewer, so graptolites indicate the age of rocks.

EARLY PALEOZOIC LIFE

Joint-legged creatures, among them crabs and lobsters, scuttle over the sea bed kicking up sand flurries. Burrowing animals such as tube worms pull into their lairs, and shell-fish clam up into the safety of their shells. The soft worms and jellyfish of former times are still to be seen, but now the sea bed really belongs to the armored hordes, the crustaceans.

At the beginning of the Cambrian period 590 million years ago – the dawn of the Paleozoic – a remarkable change swept through the living seas of the world. Suddenly all kinds of animals developed hard shells. Scientists do not know why this happened. It is possible that the steady build-up of oxygen in the atmosphere and the ocean of the time – the by-product of a flourishing underwater plant life – produced the right conditions for the shell-building biological processes to occur. On the other hand, the important factor may have been the level of minerals dissolved in the water reaching the sea from rivers. These minerals could have been taken up by the animals and secreted as shells.

Whatever happened, this sudden evolution had a great effect on the fossil record. From then onwards the rocks are full of fossils shells.

CHANGING WORLD

The continents of the world are constantly moving, and we would not have recognized the geography of the world in Cambrian times. Not only were the continents of different shapes and in different positions, but they were also awash, with the seas flooding their edges to a greater extent than ever before. This produced huge areas of warm shallow water, which may have been another influence on the evolution of new animal types.

In the following Ordovician period, 505 to 438 million years ago, the seas at first pulled back from the continents. Then they flooded over them again, producing the widest areas of continental seas known from geological history. At the end of the period an ice age began, and spread glaciers and ice sheets outwards from the poles.

The final period of the early Paleozoic was the Silurian, 438 to 408 million years ago, during which the ice melted and shallow seas spread once more. At some stage in this period the first land plants appeared.

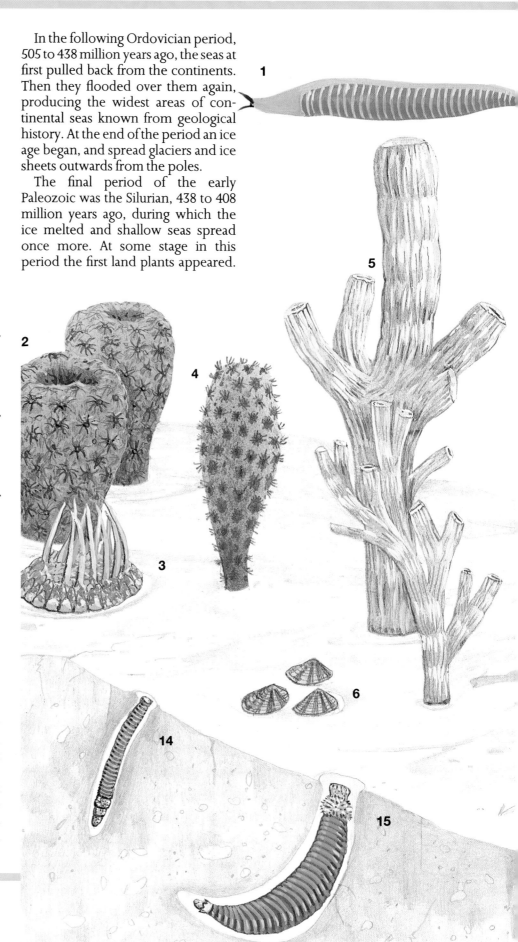

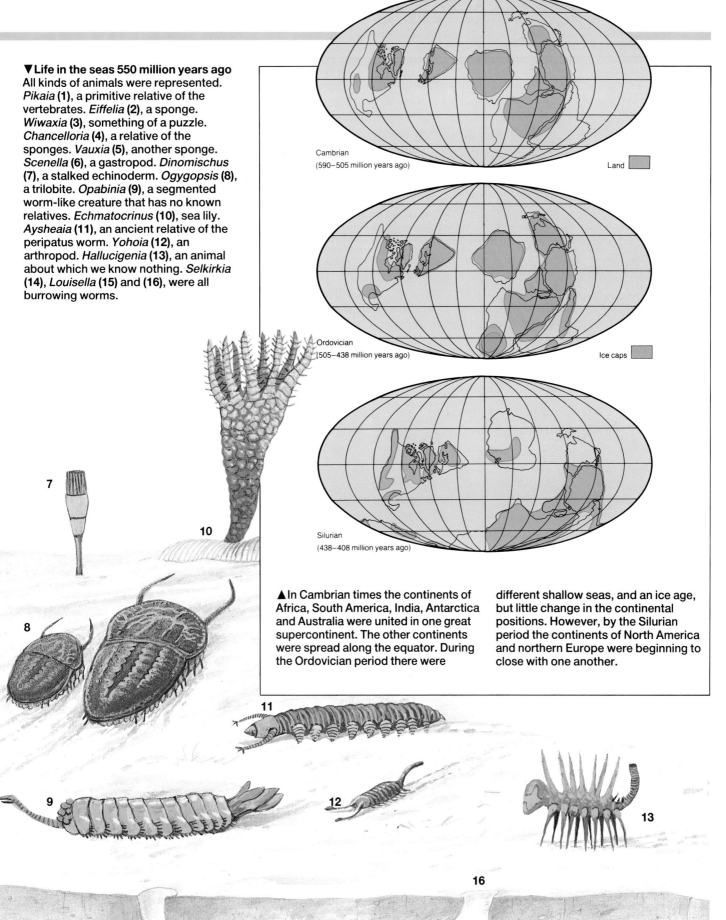

▼**Life in the seas 550 million years ago**
All kinds of animals were represented. *Pikaia* (1), a primitive relative of the vertebrates. *Eiffelia* (2), a sponge. *Wiwaxia* (3), something of a puzzle. *Chancelloria* (4), a relative of the sponges. *Vauxia* (5), another sponge. *Scenella* (6), a gastropod. *Dinomischus* (7), a stalked echinoderm. *Ogygopsis* (8), a trilobite. *Opabinia* (9), a segmented worm-like creature that has no known relatives. *Echmatocrinus* (10), sea lily. *Aysheaia* (11), an ancient relative of the peripatus worm. *Yohoia* (12), an arthropod. *Hallucigenia* (13), an animal about which we know nothing. *Selkirkia* (14), *Louisella* (15) and (16), were all burrowing worms.

Cambrian
(590–505 million years ago)

Land ▮

Ordovician
(505–438 million years ago)

Ice caps ▮

Silurian
(438–408 million years ago)

▲In Cambrian times the continents of Africa, South America, India, Antarctica and Australia were united in one great supercontinent. The other continents were spread along the equator. During the Ordovician period there were different shallow seas, and an ice age, but little change in the continental positions. However, by the Silurian period the continents of North America and northern Europe were beginning to close with one another.

45

Also the continents were gradually moving towards each other, and conditions were gradually becoming suitable for animal life to exist on land.

ODDITIES AND SUCCESSES

The evolution of invertebrates shows that the beginning of the Cambrian period brought a sudden flowering of animals with hard shells and external skeletons.

All kinds of creatures came into being at once. Many of them have descendants and counterparts today, for instance sponges, scallops and limpets. Others were very strange indeed, and scientists understand little about them from what remains are left. It seemed as if nature had discovered the secret of producing hard shells, as protective covers, and then started to experiment madly to try to see what was the best shape of animal to be equipped with them. Most of these oddities died out within a few millions years – relatively fast in geological terms – leaving a wide selection of creatures that were successful and were to continue for quite some time.

The echinoderms, the spiny-skinned invertebrates, evolved all sorts of body shapes and forms at the beginning of the Cambrian, but natural selection in time reduced these to their now traditional forms. Most types had a radial symmetry, a body divided into similar parts laid out around a central axis, like the slices of a cake. The body shape spread out in all directions from a single point, producing forms with spreading arms, for example starfish and sea lilies and rounded bun-like shapes, as in the sea urchins. Others developed a bilateral symmetry, with body divisions arranged either side of the mid-line. Their bodies had an up and a down, a front and a back, resulting in long worm-like shapes like that of the sea cucumbers.

ANCESTRAL WORMS

The arthropods, the jointed-legged animals, were the most spectacular early animals. They probably evolved from segmented worms, with each segment developing a hard shell and a pair of legs. Many types of trilobites evolved during the Cambrian. The most primitive consisted of a head-shield and a series of segments that dwindled in size towards the tail.

More advanced forms had the end segments fused into a tailshield that was sometimes as large as the head. Under the head was a mouth which opened into a stomach that filled most of the head space. The animal ate as it walked along the sea floor. Each leg had a paddle-like attachment that swept food up towards the mouth as the leg moved back and forth. Other early arthropods were shrimp-like animals that seemed to evolve no further and eventually died out.

The molluscs probably also evolved from some kind of worm, but most likely a flatworm and not a segmented one. This occurred about 500 million years ago. Of the molluscs, the gastropods were among the first to appear, and the early Cambrian sea floor must have had a large and varied fauna of sea snails and limpets.

The very first sea shells were not the bivalves, but the brachiopods. Although unrelated to the bivalves, they evolved to look like them because they had the same life-style. They remained attached to the sea bed and filtered food from the water that passed between the gaping shells. Modern brachiopods include all the lamp shells.

THE MAIN FAMILIES SETTLE

In the Ordovician period, no new major groups of animals came into existence. Instead, those that had proved themselves during the Cambrian expanded and varied in form.

Among the molluscs, the bivalves, of which the mussels are the most familiar present-day types, became numerous, but never as common or widespread as the unrelated brachiopods. The cephalopods, now represented by the squids, cuttlefish and octopuses, also became highly

▶ Cambrian life included a wild variety of shelled animals, including *Helicionella* (1), the coral-like *Coscinocyathus* (2), the trilobite *Olenus* (3), and the bivalve *Lingulella* (4).

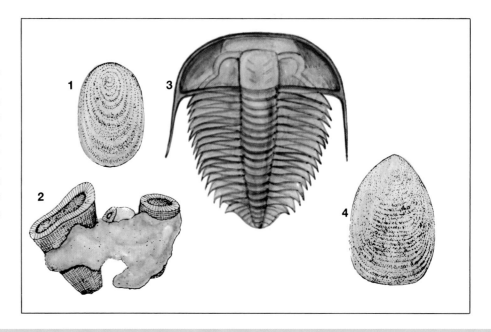

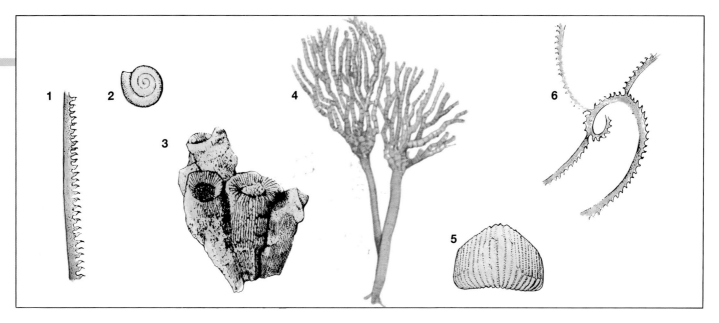

▲ Silurian life included the graptolites like *Monograptus* (1) and *Cyrtograptus* (6), gastropods like *Platyschisma* (2), corals such as *Kodonophyllum* (3), sea lilies like *Gissocrinus* (4), and brachiopods such as *Trigonirhynchia* (5).

important. Many octopus-like animals existed at that time, most of them in long conical or horn-shaped shells.

Graptolites, simple group-living creatures, had actually evolved in the Cambrian, but in the Ordovician they became the varied group that we know them to be. The first types were fan-shaped and anchored to the sea bed, but as time continued they reduced their number of branches until a bunch of about eight was the common form.

The trilobites were now doing well. Some were broad and flat and lived on the sea bed, eating food that gathered on the sandy, muddy floor. Some were spade-shaped and burrowed into the sand, feeding on buried organisms or catching food that floated by the burrow entrance. Lightweight forms, spindly shaped and covered in spines, floated above the surface, feeding on drifting food particles. Streamlined forms were active swimmers and hunters.

SOME NATURAL PUZZLES
Among the echinoderms there was a strange creature that looked as if a sea lily had fallen on to its side and become squashed. This is called a calcichordate, and is thought by some paleontologists to be the ancestor of the vertebrates, the backboned animals. What looks like a stalk was probably a tail that the animal used to push its way along the sea bed. A series of marks along its sides could be ancestral gill slits, the respiratory openings of fish and amphibians.

Some of the most useful zone fossils of the early Paleozoic are the conodonts. Each was a small worm-like creature with a fish-like fin on the tail. The teeth were made of calcite, but strengthened with a phosphate compound called apatite. This is the same mixture of substances that forms the bones of vertebrates. Some scientists think that creatures like the conodont animal are more likely to be the ancestors of the vertebrates than were the calcichordates.

After this great Ordovician burst of activity, in which many different forms were produced from a few families, evolution seemed to quieten down for many millions of years.

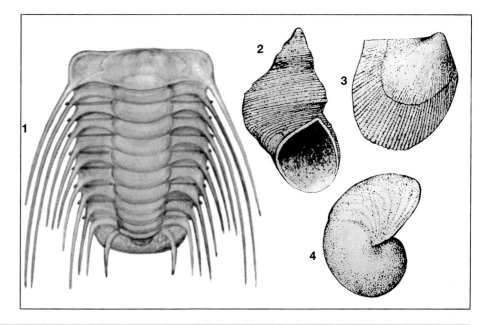

▶ Ordovician seas were misty with the many-spined trilobite *Selenopeltis* (1), gastropods like *Cyclonema* (2), bivalves such as *Byssonychia* (3) and cephalopods like *Sinuites* (4).

FOSSIL FISH

A paleontologist compares the anatomy of a fossil fish 440 million years old with that of a modern species dissected and laid out in front of him on his laboratory bench. The two are very similar: streamlined body, a rounded head, pairs of fins, and internal organs supported by a framework slung from an articulated rod, the backbone. The paleontologist is tracing the development of the basic design for the most successful of water life.

The earliest fish were hardly fish at all. They had a long thin torpedo-shaped body, several pairs of fins and a spinal cord supported by a backbone and connected to a box containing the brain. But they had no jaws. Instead the mouth was a sucker-like organ like that of the modern lamprey or hagfish. The backbone was not made of bone at all, but of a gristly substance called cartilage. The more advanced of these jawless fish did develop bone, but on the outside as an armor covering, not as an internal framework. The respiratory organs, the gills, situated immediately behind the head, were supported by rib-like struts of cartilage. Eventually the first pair of these became modified into jaws. The bony plates on the skin around the mouth then developed into teeth.

CARTILAGE AND ARMOR

The more advanced fish developed along two main evolutionary lines. All types developed complex internal skeletons, but in the first line the skeleton was made of cartilage, as in ancestral fish. These were very successful, and some evolved into the present day sharks, rays and skates. The modern cartilaginous species are like those that evolved in the Devonian period 400 million years ago.

Other early cartilaginous fish were not so successful. A group known as the placoderms had their heads and forequarters covered with heavy armor. These species did not survive the Devonian.

BONES, AIRS SACS AND RAY-FINS

In the second line of evolution of fish bone developed instead of the softer cartilage. These types also developed scales, and internal air sacs that helped them to float. In one group of bony fish, called the lobe-fins on account of their fins being supported by fleshy lobes, these air sacs developed into lungs, which allowed the fish to breathe air. Some of these lung fish gave rise to amphibians and in time to the mammals. In another group, known as the ray-fins because their fins were supported by a fan-like structure of fine spines, the air sac developed into a swimbladder. These fish could use the swimbladder to adjust their buoyancy. Ray-finned species are the most common fish of modern seas.

► The modern ray-finned fish developed in the Jurassic period about 150 million years ago. Most of today's fish were represented in the Tertiary period.

▼ *Knightia*, a fossil fish found in the Green River rock formation, Wyoming, western USA.

▼ *Hemicyclaspis* (1) was a jawless fish, *Coccosteus* (2) a placoderm, *Cladoselache* (3) an early shark, and *Eusthenopteron* (4) a lobe-fin. They were all from the seas of the Devonian period.

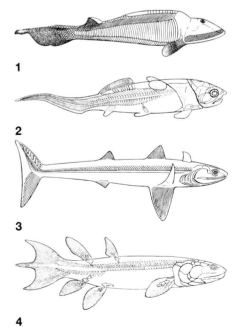

1

2

3

4

FOSSIL AMPHIBIANS

The Sun's rays have dried up the pond, stranding a lobe-finned fish on the sticky mud. Around it the other inhabitants of the pool lie dry and dying. Yet there is still water a few yards away.

With an unaccustomed action, the fish wriggles along on its muscular fins, and gulping air down into its air sac. Success! Just before the air sac dries out and its muscles become fatigued, the fish reaches the next pond and safety.

▶The fins of a lobe-finned fish such as *Eusthenopteron* (1) were packed with a network of bones that gave them strength and support. The bones later developed into a land-walking limb with well defined elbow and wrist joints, as in the earliest amphibians like *Ichthyostega* (2). The tiny bones at the tip became organized into the bones of five toes. This was the basic limb-design for all land-living vertebrates that subsequently evolved.

▼As in modern amphibians, the female *Ichthyostega* probably laid masses of eggs that were fertilized by the males outside the body. The larvae would then have lived in the water until mature.

Some of the early lobe-finned fish had the ability to live for a time on land, but they could not be regarded as land animals. The first backboned land animals were the amphibians.

Scientists are not certain about the reason for the move from a water-living to a land-living life-style. Possibly the ability to live on land enabled fish to survive the periodic drying out of lakes. Or perhaps the waters were becoming too dangerous with all the new kinds of meat-eating fish evolving. A third reason may be that the insects, which had developed to live among the new land plants, represented too good a food source to ignore. Whatever, the first amphibians had evolved from the lobe-finned fish by the Devonian period.

THE FIRST STEP ON TO LAND
The earliest amphibians retained many fish-like characteristics. Their skull was a simple box around the brain, there were bony scales in the belly, and there was a fin on the tail. However, they had four stout legs, each with five toes and each supported by strong limb girdles. The backbone was much stronger than that of a fish, and the ribs were thick and overlapping to protect the animals' internal organs.

Although the adult amphibian was a land-living animal, it had to return to the water to breed. The eggs were laid in water, and the young had to stay in the water as tadpoles until they were mature, as they do today.

A VARIETY OF BODY PLANS
During the Carboniferous period, 360 to 286 million years ago, the amphibians diversified greatly. There were huge alligator-like forms that cruised the waterways of the coal swamps. Little burrowing eel-like forms slithered legless through the mud. There were also squat flatfish-like forms that must have spent most of their time on the river beds.

In the following Permian period the climates became generally drier, and enormous armored amphibians evolved that were able to live in more arid lands. However, they were relatively short-lived. The true land-living vertebrates, the reptiles, were by now coming into their own, and they gradually overwhelmed many of the early amphibians. After the Permian period, the amphibians faded. The only types around today are the frogs, toads, newts and salamanders.

▼The huge terrestrial amphibians, of the Permian and Triassic periods included 13ft-long *Mastodonsaurus* (1), reptile-like *Diadectes* (2) 10ft in length, and squat *Eryops* (3) 5ft long. Their thick skins, armor scales and massive legs show that they lived mainly on land.

LATE PALEOZOIC LIFE

The landscape is slowly but surely turning green. The plants have spread from the bountiful oceans, established themselves on shore and are now colonizing the land. Swamps, deltas and river banks are a riot of stems, creepers and leaves. Hardier plants are finding a root-hold on the drier soils inland. And new types of animals are appearing, exploiting new food sources.

These changes were taking place in the Devonian period, 408 to 360 million years ago. The continents, which had been moving about on the surface of the globe ever since they had been formed, were beginning to drift together. Perhaps the most significant movement was the collision between the continents that were to become North America and northern Europe. An ocean that had existed between the two was squeezed out of existence and destroyed, its sediments being crumpled and thrown into a vast mountain range.

As soon as these mountains were thrown up, they began to be worn away or eroded. Wind, ice, rain, frost, heating by the Sun and all the other weather conditions acted on the rocks and started to break them down. Streams and rivers carried the fragments down to the lowlands and deposited them there, creating deltas.

THE AGE OF FERNS
The sandy deltas and waterways were covered with the first forests. Simple plants, consisting of little more than a green stem, had begun to colonize the land in the previous Silurian period, but now more advanced kinds were developing. These were plants that had well differentiated organs. Leaves absorbed the energy of the Sun and used it to generate food (the process of photosynthesis). Roots absorbed minerals and moisture from the soil, and a plumbing system of long thin vessels moved the food and water around the whole plant. In terms of structure and functioning, these plants had about the same level of complexity as modern ferns, and so the Devonian is often known as The Age of Ferns.

Into these early forests crept the first land animals. Insects, spiders, scorpions and other arthropods (animals with a body divided into segments and encased in a tough horny outer skeleton) evolved to feed on this vegetation and upon one another.

Following the invertebrates, came the vertebrates (animals with a backbone). Some of the lobe-finned fish evolved in such a manner they could live for a time out of water. These species were quick to exploit the readily available food supply on land. They gradually developed into the first amphibians, about 350 million years ago. Fossil specimens have been found in Greenland in sediments that contain abundant land-plant fossils.

▼ In the Devonian period, many reefs were built by the sponge-like *Stromatopora* (1). Fish ranged from the jawless *Pteraspis* (2) to the lobe-finned *Osteolepis* (3). Primitive land plants were like the stalk-like *Psilophyton* (4). Conodonts, the jaw parts of worm-like animals such as *Icriodus* (5), are common from this period. Shellfish continued to be abundant, such as the gastropod *Murchisonia* (6) and the brachiopod *Stringocephalus* (7).

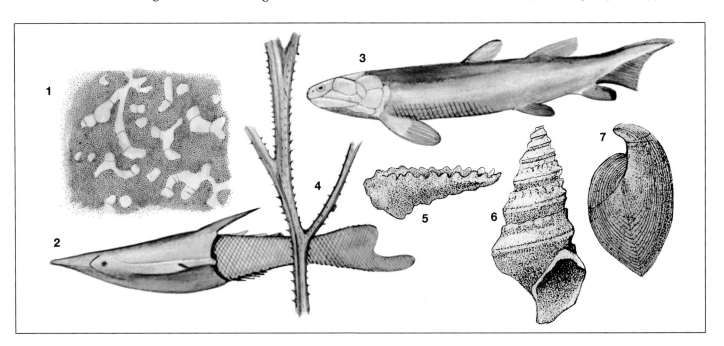

THE AGE OF FISH

It is not just the land life of Devonian times that scientists find interesting. The seas continued to be productive in terms of the evolution of new ways of living and new body shapes and forms. Another nickname for the Devonian period is The Age of Fish.

The extensive reefs – the ridges of rocks and sand that develop in warm coastal waters – which developed during the Silurian period continued into the Devonian. Now the reefs were built not by algae, but by sponge-like organisms. The different kinds of habitat provided by the reefs gave rise to a vast number of different animals. Brachiopods continued to flourish, while the shelled cephalopods developed into all kinds of new forms. However, the many graptolites became extinct, as did the swimming forms of the trilobites. By far the most important swimming creatures were now the fish. From the primitive jawless bottom-feeders there developed the shark-like cartiliginous fish, the armored placoderms and the ultimately highly successful bony fish. It was from the last group that the amphibians developed and made the big evolutionary step on to the land.

▼An ancient animal is the velvet worm *Peripatus*. Fossil marine types have been found in Cambrian rocks dating back to about 520 million years ago, and land-living forms like this one probably existed by the Devonian period.

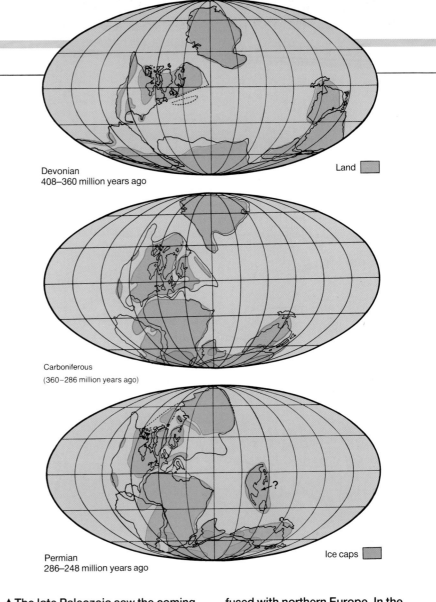

Devonian
408–360 million years ago

Land

Carboniferous
(360–286 million years ago)

Permian
286–248 million years ago

Ice caps

▲The late Paleozoic saw the coming together of the continents of the world to form the single continent Pangaea. Most of the southern continents had been united throughout the early Paleozoic. Then in the Devonian period North America fused with northern Europe. In the Carboniferous this landmass fused with Africa. In Permian times the main part of Asia also collided with Europe, giving the mountain range that survives as the Urals. Ice caps formed on the continents near the South Pole.

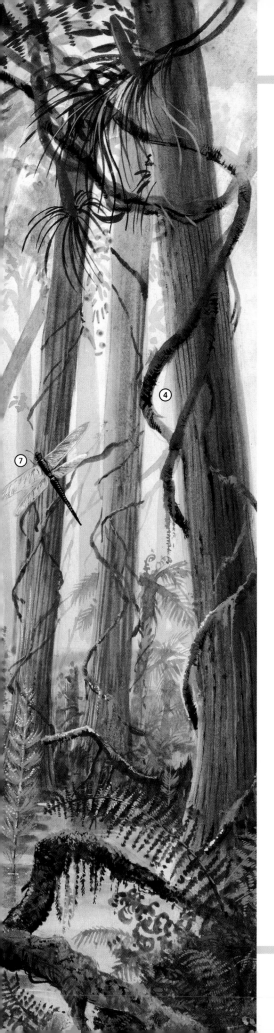

GEOLOGICAL CHANGES

As the huge mountain ranges thrown up during the Devonian period were eroded more and more during the succeeding Carboniferous, the rock debris was spread far and wide, building up lowland swamps, marshes and deltas. Meanwhile, everywhere the sea levels began to rise and the edges of all the continents became flooded. Broad, warm, shallow seas spread over the edges of the continents. Today there are vast beds of shallow-water limestones that date from this ancient time.

The Carboniferous period was relatively long, lasting from 360 to 286 million years ago. In the United States, it is regarded as two distinct periods – the Mississippian up to 320 million years ago, and the Pennsylvanian beyond that. The earlier timespan is characterized by various limestone deposits, while the later period is famous for the deposition of swamp and forest material.

During the Carboniferous period the equator ran through California, Newfoundland, the British Isles, the Netherlands and Germany. The shallow waters that flooded across the continents in these areas would have been tropical, that is, warm and clear. Reefs were again abundant, along with the varied shelly creatures that have always accompanied them. Crinoids, the stalked relatives of the starfish, were particularly common and must have formed dense waving underwater thickets.

◄The coal forests of late Carboniferous times had trees such as *Cordaites* (1) resembling a primitive conifer, *Lepidodendron* (2) and *Sigillaria* (6), which were giant club mosses, and *Calamites* (10), a giant horsetail. Around the rootstocks and stumps of the club mosses (5) grew ferns (3) and horsetail creepers (4). Huge dragonflies like *Meganeura* (7) and giant millipedes such as *Arthropleura* (9) lived here, and big amphibians, for example *Eogyrinus* (8) and *Eryops* (11) wallowed.

SWAMPED WITH GIANT PLANTS

As the eroded material was washed down from the mountains and out into the shallow seas, it would have been the finest and lightest fragments that were carried farthest from the shores. They would have been deposited as mud or silt on the sea floor. Then, as the river mouths built out as deltas, the coarser sand would be washed out to sea and deposited on top of the mud. Eventually, this sand would have been built up until it formed a sandbank above water level. Once this happened, plants would immediately have taken root and formed swamps adjoining the deltas.

Under the humid tropical conditions vast forests built up across the deltas and swamps. These consisted of great examples of horsetails as big as Christmas trees and club moss trees the size of redwoods. At the bases of these plants was a thick undergrowth of ferns, and creeping horsetails entwined everything. Each time the sea level rose again, which happened on many occasions, the forests were flooded and a new deposit of marine sediment was formed. The cycle of mud, sand and forest deposits was repeated several times.

COAL SEAMS DEVELOP

The rocks of the late Carboniferous period show this cyclical arrangement. A bed of limestone is followed by a bed of shale which has formed from the mud. This in turn is covered by a bed of sandstone. The top of the sandstone has plant roots embedded in it, and above this is a layer of coal. Coal is a carbon-rich deposit derived from the build-up and chemical and physical alteration of ancient plants. It is the remains of the Carboniferous forests that produce most of the economic coalfields of the world.

The coal forests were full of animal life. Millipedes as long as snakes burrowed through the soggy leaf litter, while dragonfly species as large

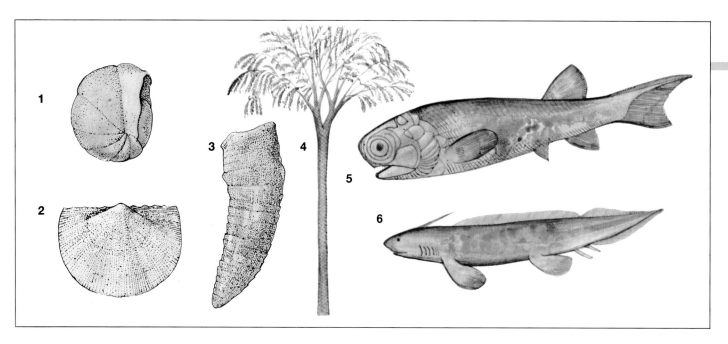

as macaws flitted between the tree trunks. The shallow waters were full of fish that were pursued by alligator-like amphibians. Most importantly, the first true land-living animals, the reptiles, had evolved in the early Carboniferous, and they were probably abundant among the trees of the late Carboniferous period.

ICE SHEETS IN GONDWANA
At the end of the Carboniferous period there was an ice age in the far south. Great ice sheets and glaciers covered southern landmasses. They gouged up soil and rocks, carried them along and then dumped them in strange heaps along their edges and at their mouths. They also scraped clean exposed rock surfaces, polishing them flat and gouging out deep scratch marks in them.

By today's distribution of landmasses on the Earth, this would seem to be a particularly wide area to be affected by a single ice age. However, at that time, some 280 million years ago, all the southern continents were fused together as one landmass known as Gondwana.

THE NEW RED SANDSTONE
Elsewhere on the globe there was a general, but less marked, change in climate conditions as the Carboniferous period passed into the Permian

period. The end of the Permian, 248 million years ago, marks the end of the Paleozoic era.

The coming together of all the continents caused a general uplift and gradually the shallow seas drained away from the continental edges. Deserts spread across the lands once more, so that the typical rocks that formed in Permian times were desert sandstones. Examining these today, we can see the shapes of the Permian sand dunes. These rocks are often called the New Red Sandstones to distinguish them from those that formed in the Devonian period.

In rock layers in present-day Europe and North America, the Old Red Sandstones are followed by the tropical limestones and forest deposits of the Carboniferous and then by the New Red Sandstones of the Permian. Scientists have taken this sequence to indicate that between about 400 and 250 million years ago the areas drifted from the Earth's desert belt in the Southern hemisphere, across the rain forest zone of the equator, and into the desert belt of the Northern hemisphere.

REPTILES TAKE OVER
With the coming of the drier conditions came the evolution of a new selection of animals more suited than their predecessors to the prevailing

▲ Carboniferous sea life was varied and included cephalopods – octopus-like animals in coiled shells – such as *Goniatites* (1) and brachiopods like *Rugosochonetes* (2). Corals were plentiful and most were of the single horn-shaped type, for instance *Palaeosmilia* (3). In the coal swamps a typical Club moss tree was *Lepidodendron* (4). Fish were common, such as the ray-finned *Cornuboniscus* (5) and the shark *Xenacanthus* (6).

conditions. Amphibians generally prefer moist places as they need water in which to breed and lay their eggs. However, during the Permian period they flourished in what little fresh water there was. Some developed into heavily armored land-living types.

It was the reptiles that really came into their own in the Permian. They had evolved in the Carboniferous as small lizard-like creatures, but now they were developing into a wide variety of different types.

The most successful were a large group commonly referred to as the mammal-like reptiles. The earliest of these were the pelycosaurs, which were animals that looked like big lizards, but had "sails" on their backs. Some were meat-eaters, but many types ate plants. It seems that the sails were a primitive heat-regulating device. They consisted of a sheet of skin stretched between bony projections from the spine. Early in the mornings the animals would hold the sails in the position that would enable them to absorb the maximum amount of the Sun's rays and so heat up their blood quickly and efficiently. When they became too hot, they would hold the sails away from the Sun or into the wind to cool off.

Later types of mammal-like reptiles had better heat-regulating systems. These resembled the heat loss and heat gain mechanisms involved in the "warm-bloodedness" of all the true mammals, for example sweating and control of bloodflow. These more advanced reptiles had also abandoned the lizard-like appearance, and developed long running legs that were held directly beneath them like those of mammals. The other main group of reptiles that developed in the Permian were the archosaurs. These tended to be more crocodile-like, but again with legs that could be tucked underneath their bodies.

A DRAMATIC CHANGE

At the end of the Permian there was a mass extinction. About 30 percent of the plant and animal families present at the time soon died out especially those in the sea. The trilobites finally disappeared, along with many types of brachiopods and corals.

Scientists do not know exactly how or why this extinction took place, but it might have been a consequence of the coming together of all the continents. This would have affected the saltiness of the sea. Alternatively, there may have been a change in the oxygen content of the atmosphere because of the widespread deserts. Whatever the cause, it cleared the way for the development of new groups of animals.

◀Thick beds of limestone were still being laid down in the shallow seas of Permian times. This is the most famous bed, the Kaibab limestone in the Grand Canyon, USA.

▼The most significant type of Permian plant was a kind of fern that reproduced by a seed, for example *Glossopteris* (1). This existed throughout the Southern hemisphere. Among the animals *Dimetrodon* (2) was a typical pelycosaur, and *Eryops* (3) was a land-living amphibian. In the sea a common brachiopod was *Dielasma* (4), and many of the marine beds can be dated by microscopic organisms such as *Nodosinella* (5).

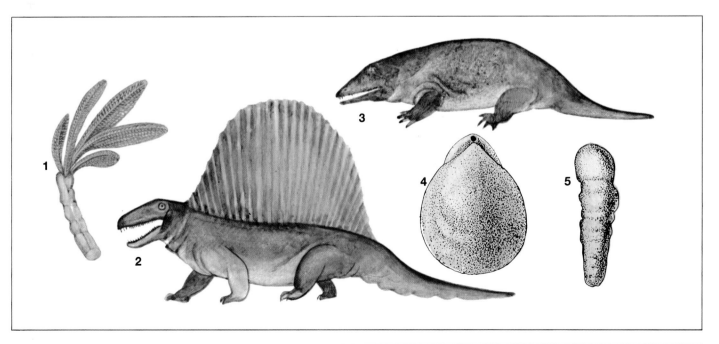
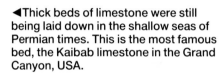

FOSSIL REPTILES

A lizard scampers over the sand, darting after an insect to eat. It captures the insect then withdraws timidly into the safety of a shady crack between rocks. Bigger and more dangerous animals are about so the lizard is constantly alert. All this could also have happened 250 million years ago, when the lizard's ancestors included the biggest and most varied, widespread and successful animals that ever lived on Earth.

The ancestors of today's amphibians were very successful as land animals, but of all the vertebrates (backboned animals) it was the reptiles that well and truly conquered the land.

The reason for the reptiles' success is their egg. Amphibians need to return to water to breed and to lay their eggs, and the young have to go through an aquatic stage before becoming sufficiently mature to come out on land. The reptile egg acts as a self-contained pond in which the young animal grows to maturity. It has a tough outer leathery shell that lets oxygen in and carbon dioxide out, but prevents the escape of water and fluids bathing the embryo. Also, there is a yolk that acts as a food supply until

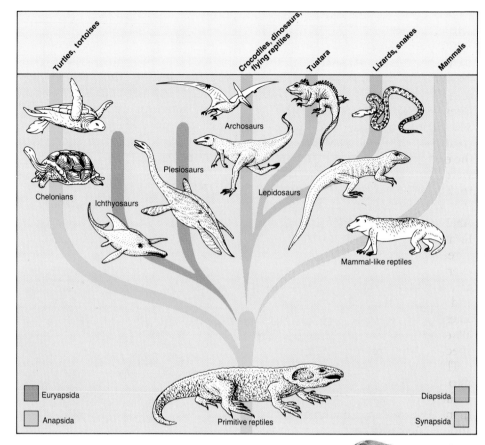

Euryapsida · Anapsida · Diapsida · Synapsida

▲Early lizard-like reptiles gave rise to all the later forms, and also to the mammals and the birds.

the young animal is old enough to break free of the shell. An adult reptile has a skin that is waterproof and prevents the animal from drying out.

Reptiles evolved from amphibians of some kind in the swamps and forests of Carboniferous times, about 340 million years ago. A lizard-like creature about 8in long, *Westlothiana*, is the earliest known reptile. Its remains were found in the early Carboniferous rocks of Scotland.

AN EXTENDED FAMILY

From these beginnings the reptiles spread all over the Earth, adopting every life-style. There were, and still are, crawling reptiles, climbing ones, and reptiles that run, swim and fly. These different means of movement all evolved again and again among species in different reptile groups.

The reptile family tree soon split into four main branches. Scientists define each branch by the arrangement of bones in the animals' skulls and, in particular, by the number and position of the gaps between the bones behind the eye sockets. The branch that gave rise to the turtles and their allies comprised species with no gaps in the skull behind these sockets. The branch leading to the dinosaurs and most modern reptiles included animals with two pairs of gaps. A third

▼►A variety of reptiles
A selection of extinct reptiles that evolved in Mesozoic times. *Saltoposuchus* (1), typical of the crocodile-like animals from which the dinosaurs evolved. *Cetiosaurus* (2), a long-necked plant-eating dinosaur. *Thrinaxodon* (3), one of the small reptiles that gave rise to the mammals. *Stenopterygius* (4), a marine species. *Plesiosaurus* (5), a fish-eater. *Bradysaurus* (6), an early plant-eating reptile. *Champsosaurus* (7), an animal like a crocodile that lived on after the dinosaurs. *Corythosaurus* (8), a plant-eating dinosaur that stood upright on its hind legs. *Pterodactylus* (9), one of the flying reptiles, the pterosaurs.

branch, which eventually gave rise to the mammals, consisted of reptiles with a pair of gaps situated low down on the skull. The branch from which the most important swimming reptiles eventually evolved comprised species with one pair situated high up on the skull.

The first reptiles were lizard-like animals and mostly ate the abundant insects, spiders and centipedes that infested the forests and swamps of the Carboniferous period. Many of them may have been water-living creatures, competing directly with the amphibians in their environment.

A RETURN TO THE SEA

Although the reptiles evolved as land-living animals, immediately many of them adapted back to life in the sea. This happened in many different reptile groups in Permian and Triassic times. In most cases, the long, lizard tail became flattened and adapted for use as a paddle, and the feet became webbed. The teeth reflected well the animals' diets – sharp, pointed teeth for fish-eaters like *Askeptosaurus*, and fine comb-like teeth for plankton-eaters such as *Mesosaurus*. *Placodus*, which fed on shellfish, evolved many knobbly crushing teeth.

Some 50 million years later, many large specialized swimming reptiles evolved, with paddles for limbs. The plesiosaurs had a turtle-like body and a long snake-like neck. The related pliosaurs had a short neck and elongated head and resembled whales. The ichthyosaurs were the ultimate in marine reptiles. They were almost dolphin-like in their streamlined shapes, their paddles, their fins and their jaws, which were highly adapted for catching fish.

Nevertheless, all these specialized swimming reptiles died out, except for one group. From this group the true turtles evolved in Triassic times, and they have survived almost unchanged until today.

▲ Scientists know that the dinosaurs laid eggs because they found their nests. These are eggs of *Protoceratops*, an armored dinosaur. They are about 8in long.

► The early reptiles became so successful on land because of their hard-shelled eggs, which were like those of a modern crocodile. The shell and its membranes prevented the egg from drying out, but still let in oxygen.

▼ We know so much about the reptiles of the past because their bones have been found in Mesozoic rocks from all over the world. Most dinosaur bones lie in rocks formed from the sediments of ancient rivers.

LIFE IN THE SKY

Among the early insects, flying species quickly evolved. The same happened with the reptiles. The earliest flying reptiles were mere gliders, riding on warm currents of air between cliff-faces and rocks by means of webs of skin stretched across horizontal ribs. They resembled the modern flying lizards, or dragons, common in the forests of Southeast Asia.

Flying, as a means of movement, developed to the greatest degree among the pterosaurs. These reptiles had wings of skin supported by their arms and lengthened fourth fingers. They were warm-blooded animals, hairy as bats, and flew with an active flapping motion just like birds. Early forms, such as *Dimorphodon*, had a long tail for steering, but later types, for instance *Pterodactylus*, were able to maneuvre just as well without a tail. *Quetzalcoatlus* of Cretaceous times, with a 40ft wingspan, was probably the biggest flying animal ever.

LANDLUBBERS

Perhaps the most successful of the reptiles were the dinosaurs – the "terrible lizards." Certainly they are the most famous. They arose from the great mass of different reptile types in the late Triassic period 220 million years ago. Their immediate ancestors were crocodile-like archosaurs that had a long tail and long hind legs. In water, these were used for swimming. On land, the hind legs could support the animals' bodies and the tail used for balance. The bipedal stance of the typical dinosaur soon evolved.

The first dinosaurs were all meat-eaters and active hunters. Then the plant-eaters evolved. These had a heavy body – a bigger gut is needed to digest plant material – and so they moved around on all four of their limbs (quadrupedal stance). They evolved a long neck to enable them to reach food high up in trees.

Later plant-eaters had modified hips that enabled them to walk on just their hind legs yet still support the big gut. Some of these species developed horns as weapons and protective armor, and they acquired the bizarre shapes that are now so familiar to us.

▼Although it was the special type of egg that gave reptiles their success, some species developed the technique of live birth. The fish-like *Ichthyosaurus* could not lay eggs on land, and so the young matured inside its mother's body, as this fossil shows.

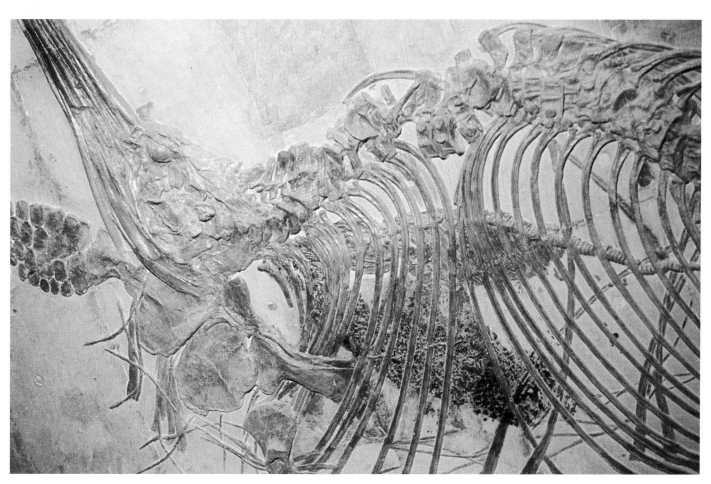

EARLY MESOZOIC LIFE

Horsetails cover the banks of gravelly streams that flow from the hills. These are not the vast tree-like horsetails that choked the Carboniferous swamps, but small wispy types. The trees of the nearby forest are no longer club mosses but graceful conifers like the present-day monkey-puzzles. The landscape has changed, and so has the plant – and animal – life. New species are evolving all the time.

At the end of the Permian period, 248 million years ago, there was carnage – widespread death, which geologists call a mass extinction. At that time, 96 percent of all the species of marine animals became extinct. The horn-shaped corals, the trilobites, most of the brachiopods and a large number of echinoderms, all died out. It was probably not a sudden event, but happened over a few million years. However, in geological terms this is a mere blink of the eye. The evolution of new forms that took their places marked the first of the three periods of the Mesozoic era. This is known as the Triassic period, the second and third periods being the Jurassic and the Cretaceous.

NEW PLANTS SPREAD
On dry land, the changes may not have been so noticeable. By the Triassic, the continents had fused into a single landmass, Pangaea, and deserts

continued to spread far and wide. The tall mountain ranges thrown up in the Permian period were gradually being worn down into hills. In the damp areas, however, the vegetation was changing considerably. The huge club moss trees and the gigantic horsetails had died out and were being replaced by coniferous (cone-bearing) trees and relatives of the palm-like cycads. The seed-bearing ferns became extinct and spore-bearing species, like all present-day ferns, took their place.

Among the animals, the great amphibians of Carboniferous times had died out. Reptiles had evolved and were developing into all kinds of strange forms. During the late Permian period, many of these soon died out, but the most successful were about to rule both the Triassic and Jurassic periods, 248 to 144 million years ago.

ARCHOSAURS AND AMMONITES
A very important Permian group of animals had been the mammal-like reptiles. During the Triassic, these faded away, but not before their descendants, the true mammals, had evolved. The early mammals were

▶ A variety of early Mesozoic animals
Scaphonyx (1), a plant-eater.
Kannemeyeria (2), one of the last of the primitive mammal-like reptiles.
Euparkeria (3), a primitive archosaur.
Scelidosaurus (4), one of the earliest plant-eating dinosaurs. *Saltopus* (5), a meat-eating dinosaur. *Mystriosuchus* (6), a phytosaur, a crocodile-like archosaur.
Thrinaxodon (7), an advanced mammal-like reptile. *Erythrosuchus* (8), a huge and powerful archosaur.

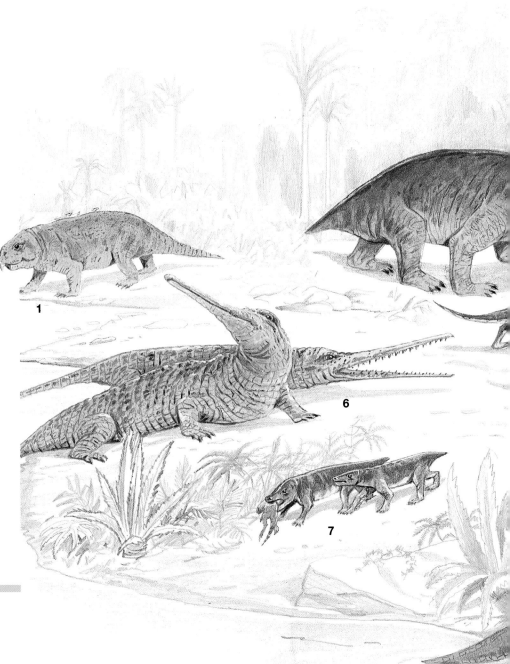

small and mouse-like. They did not develop into any especially important species for many millions of years. The animals that did take over immediately from the mammal-like reptiles were a group called the archosaurs.

Modern crocodiles are archosaurs, and their ancestors were very similar creatures. Several different types evolved, and they spread into all the habitats on land. In time, they became the first of the dinosaurs.

About 213 million years ago, the Triassic period slipped into the Jurassic. At the beginning of that period,

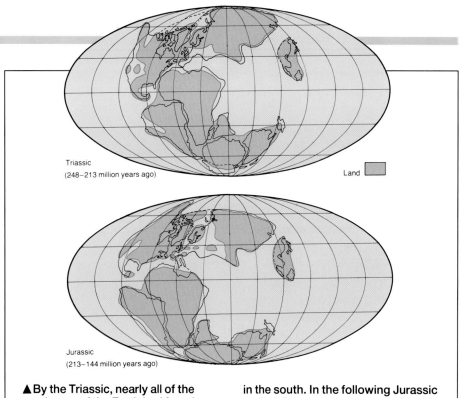

Triassic
(248–213 million years ago)

Land

Jurassic
(213–144 million years ago)

▲ By the Triassic, nearly all of the continents of the Earth had fused together to form a single supercontinent called Pangaea. This was divided into two main parts – Laurasia in the north and Gondwana in the south. In the following Jurassic period, Pangaea began to crack up. At the same time, shallow seas spread over the edges and what had been deserts became moist fertile lowlands.

the supercontinent of Pangaea was still intact, but the sea level was starting to rise around its edges. Shallow seas flooded across the lower-lying areas, bringing much moister conditions to the heart of the great landmass. Deserts gave way to damp forests and swamps once more.

Layers of limestone rock, formed from the shells of dead marine invertebrates, were again laid down in shallow seas. However, the fossils that geologists find in them are different from those found in earlier rocks. The fossil record shows that brachiopods were still present in the Jurassic, but they were rapidly giving way to the more modern bivalve molluscs. The most important of the molluscs of that time, though, were the ammonites. These resembled octopuses, each encased in a coiled shell. The shell differed from one species to the next. Most kinds were the size of coins, but a few were as large as bus wheels. Each species evolved and became extinct so quickly that each bed of Jurassic marine rock can be dated by the ammonite fossils it contains.

REPTILES RULE THE SEAS
With the Jurassic seas full of shoals of ammonites, there were many larger creatures around to eat them. The ichthyosaurs, or fish lizards – streamlined dolphin-like reptiles with paddles and fins – hunted ammonites through the clear water. Ichthyosaur

◄**Reptiles of the Jurassic period**
The ammonite-strewn early Jurassic shoreline by the shallow seas of southern England shows representative reptiles of the time. A dead *Stenopterygius* (1), a species of ichthyosaur, is washed up. A group of the plesiosaur *Plesiosaurus* (2) flop back to the sea having laid their eggs in the sand. They are disturbed by the roar of the theropod *Megalosaurus* (3), as it attacks an armored *Scelidosaurus* (4). The pterosaur *Dimorphodon* (5) flies overhead.

skeletons have been found with masses of tiny ammonite fragments in the stomach area.

Ichthyosaurs also ate fish, as did the other sea reptiles of the time. The most primitive group of ray-finned fish, the chondrosteans, with thick bony scales and shark-like tails, died away at the end of the Paleozoic. They were replaced by the holosteans, with simpler scales and tail and a more complex jaw structure. The modern Gar pike is one of the few surviving holosteans. Plesiosaurs, sea reptiles with their paddle-like limbs and long neck, darted after these fish.

RISE OF THE DINOSAURS
On the land surface, the dinosaurs had taken over. Among them, the two-footed meat-eaters – called the theropods because of the mammal-like structure of the foot (in Greek, *thero* means wild beast, *podos* a foot) – hunted everywhere. The long-necked plant-eaters – known as sauropods on account of the lizard-like structure of the foot – were also widespread and common. By now, the two-footed plant-eating dinosaurs had also evolved, and they browsed on the ferny vegetation. These were the ornithopods; their feet were like those of birds. From the ornithopod line, the first armored dinosaurs had also developed.

The theropods preyed on all large animals, including other dinosaurs. The sauropods defended themselves against the theropods using their huge bodies; they would try to push them away. The ornithopods could run away. The armored dinosaurs, such as *Stegosaurus*, were well protected by their bony plates, horns and thick neck frills. The members of the other line of archosaurs, the crocodiles, had also established themselves and were as successful in the sluggish rivers then as they are today.

While this balance of power was maintaining itself on the ground, the trees and the skies echoed to the calls of the pterosaurs, the flying reptiles. The Mesozoic had indeed become the Age of Reptiles.

A WORLDWIDE FAUNA

In the later part of the Jurassic period the continents began to break apart. The rifts that appeared across Pangaea got wider and longer. The northern mass of Laurasia began to separate from southern Gondwana. A giant crack appeared in the land between what was to become Africa and India, and another developed between what would eventually be India and Antarctica. At the same time, great mountain ridges were being built up on the sea bed, and the water that these displaced spread over the continents as shallow seas. By the end of the period a quarter of the continental area of Earth was covered by shallow water.

Despite the breakup of continents and the spreading of the seas, the animal life tended to be the same the world over. In North America, in a strip of open lowland between the newly rising Rocky Mountains and a vast shallow inland sea that was spreading southwards across the center of the continent, there lived some of the most famous dinosaurs. Through the riverside woodlands roamed herds of big sauropods, for example, *Diplodocus*, *Apatosaurus* and *Brachiosaurus*. These were hunted by great meat-eating theropods like *Ceratosaurus* and *Allosaurus*, and smaller hunters like *Ornitholestes*. Ornithopods that included *Camptosaurus*, and armored dinosaurs such as *Stegosaurus*, lived here too.

Across the world, on the shoreline of East Africa, where rivers were flowing out into the sea that was opening between Africa and India, the same kinds of animals lived. Here, fossil-hunters have found skeletons of *Brachiosaurus* and a small relative of *Diplodocus* called *Dicraeosaurus*. Kentrosaurus was the local version of

Stegosaurus, and there were small *Camptosaurus*-like ornithopods known as *Dysalotosaurus*. These were hunted by such theropods as *Megalosaurus*. Pterosaurs like *Rhamphorhynchus* flew here.

In the wooded islands that peppered the seas of northern Europe, *Megalosaurus* was still the terror of the land. In the fine limestones that were deposited at the time there are bones of the pterosaur *Rhamphorhynchus* and of the more advanced *Pterodactylus* and of the first bird, *Archaeopteryx*.

PLANTS OF THE TIME

The vegetation of the Jurassic period was similar to that of the preceding Triassic. The trees were mostly conifers and cycad relatives. However, flowering plants were beginning to appear. The undergrowth continued to consist mostly of ferns, and reed beds of horsetails grew in rivers.

In the ferny undergrowth there scuttled many small animals. The earliest lizards are known from this time. In Europe, some of the river banks were inhabited by crocodiles no larger than a yard in length. The most significant small animals, however, were the mammals. In those days, these were only little shrew-like and opossum-like beasts, and they must have spent much of their time dodging the huge feet of the big reptiles. But in time, their descendants would replace the dinosaurs as the dominant animals on Earth.

◄**A diversity of dinosaurs and other prehistoric reptiles** The coastal plain of what is now Tanzania was, in Jurassic times, populated by dinosaurs. These included *Brachiosaurus* (1), a sauropod; *Dicraeosaurus* (2), a sauropod; *Kentrosaurus* (3), an armored stegosaur; *Dysalotosaurus* (4), a small ornithopod; *Elaphrosaurus* (5), a small theropod; and *Megalosaurus* (6), a big theropod. Pterosaurs such as *Rhamphorhynchus* (7) flew in the sky, and crocodiles (8) lived in the water. The animal and plant life was like that of North America since the continents were still very close to one another.

LATE MESOZOIC LIFE

The herd of dinosaurs chomps its way across a fern-covered area. Suddenly, from the nearby oak copse, a huge flesh-eating beast emerges from among the bushes. The herd bunches up and presents a defense of horns and armor against the danger. The meat-eater gives up and stalks off down towards the forest. There will be easier prey down there. But not for long. The time of the great reptiles will soon be drawing to a close.

The Cretaceous period, which began 144 million years ago and lasted until 65 million years ago, was both the climax and the end of the Age of Reptiles. By now the continents of the Earth had well and truly broken up and were drifting far apart. As a result, different animal life was appearing in different isolated places.

A VARIED ECOLOGY

North America was still joined to Asia across the Bering Strait and so these two places were inhabited by the same beasts. Sauropod dinosaurs were slowly dying out and their places were being taken by a group of highly successful ornithopods that scientists refer to as the "duckbills." These had broad beaks adapted for chewing the new kind of vegetation that had evolved, and several species had strange crests on their heads. The horned dinosaurs, such as *Triceratops*, became plentiful, and meat-eaters, like *Tyrannosaurus*, were common.

OTHER PLACES, OTHER BEASTS

In South America, on the other hand, the sauropods were still widespread and numerous. The duckbills never gained a foothold there. Some of these sauropods, for instance *Saltasaurus*, even developed armor.

Sauropods also survived in Australia, and the island continent that was India even boasted a late-Cretaceous stegosaur, *Dravidosaurus*.

▶ Some dinosaurs of North America from the late Cretaceous period
Corythosaurus (1), a crested duckbill; *Alamosaurus* (2), one of the last of the sauropods; *Triceratops* (3), the biggest of the horned dinosaurs; *Tyrannosaurus* (4), the biggest of the meat-eaters; *Ornithomimus* (5), an ostrich-like theropod; and *Pachycephalosaurus* (6), a bone-headed ornithopod.

▶ A fossil of *Leptolepis*, a freshwater fish of the Jurassic period found in Australia. By this time kinds of fish leading to all present-day types had developed.

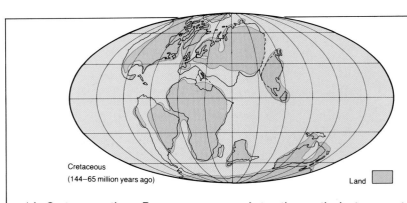

Cretaceous
(144–65 million years ago)

Land

▲ In Cretaceous times Pangaea was no more. North America had split from Europe. South America was pulling away from Africa. India was an island. However, Australia was still joined to Antarctica, as the last remnant of Gondwana. As the continents moved apart, there were huge ridges lifted up on the ocean floor, and seas spread widely over the lower areas of land.

►Representative animals in the chalk seas of Kansas at the end of the Cretaceous period *Pteranodon* (1), a big pterosaur that probably soared above the sea looking for fish; *Tylosaurus* (2), a mosasaur that may have hunted fish or ammonites; *Elasmosaurus* (3), one of the longest of the plesiosaurs with a neck that it could use to dart after fish; *Archelon* (4), a turtle as big as a motor boat; *Hesperornis* (5), a flightless diving bird like a wingless toothed penguin; and *Ichthyornis* (6), a fishing bird resembling a tern with teeth.

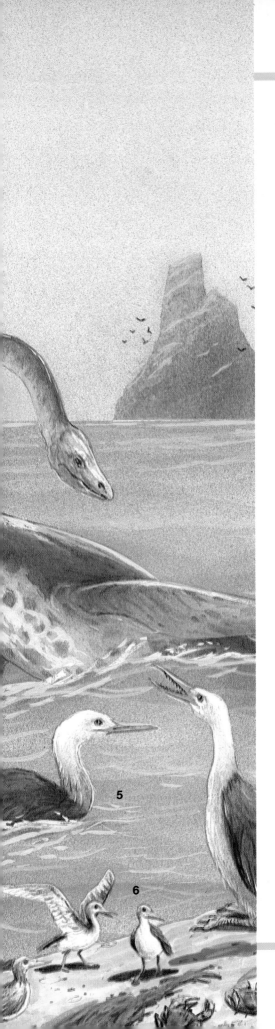

During the late Mesozoic, Australia was still a part of Antarctica. And although there have not yet been any dinosaur remains found beneath the Antarctic ice, it would seem likely that this continent would have had the same dinosaur fauna as Australia.

THE BIRTH OF FLOWERS

Although the animal life was different on every continent, there was a worldwide change sweeping through the plant life of the Cretaceous period. New types of plants had evolved and were growing everywhere. These were plants that we would recognize today – plants with flowers. Conifer trees and a rich undergrowth of ferns, club mosses and horsetails were still present then, but on the whole the dinosaurs wandered through forests that would be familiar to us.

THE CLEAR SEAS

The continents were now breaking up and moving apart on a large scale. Sea water then spilled over the edges of the continents and the shallow shelf seas became even more widespread than ever before.

The ammonites still abounded in these shallow seas. The swimming reptiles were present too, but some early forms had died out and new ones had evolved. The ichthyosaurs had disappeared. Now the main hunters of the ammonites were the mosasaurs – huge crocodile-like animals to which the modern monitor lizards are related.

The plesiosaurs developed into enormous creatures. *Elasmosaurus* had a snake-like neck consisting of more than 70 vertebrae. (All modern mammals, and humans, have only seven neck vertebrae.) The pliosaurs, too, achieved great sizes. The biggest known was *Kronosaurus* which had jaws 9ft long – about a quarter of its body length. A variety of seabirds had also evolved by this time, and pterosaurs still skimmed the sea for fish.

The types of fish that all these creatures ate were changing with time. The teleosts, which include modern fish like cod, salmon and herring, had taken over from more primitive ray-finned species. They differed from their ancestors in having symmetrical tail fins and in their complex jaws, which they could thrust out in the familiar pouting action to catch food.

AND THEN THERE WERE NONE

About 65 million years ago, at the height of all this evolutionary activity and the success of the great reptiles, another mass extinction swept the world. The dinosaurs were wiped out. So were the pterosaurs and the swimming reptiles. Among the simpler animals, the ammonites became extinct, as did most of the shelled organisms that gave rise to the beds of chalk. In all, about three-quarters of living species of animal died out.

Why did this happen? Scientists are not certain, but many believe that a giant meteorite or a swarm of comets from space struck the Earth. This accident would have sent masses of smoke, dust and steam into the atmosphere. For several months, the amount of sunlight reaching the Earth's surface would have been reduced, lowering temperatures worldwide and killing most of the plants. Extinction of plant-eaters and then meat-eaters would have taken place. The evidence for this theory is a bed of rock at the top of Cretaceous sediments which is rich in such elements as iridium normally found only in meteorites and asteroids.

An alternative theory states that the extinction may have been due to normal climatic changes caused by the movements of continents and the opening of the oceans. It seems possible that different groups of animals became extinct at different times in different places, which would give support to this idea.

FOSSIL MAMMALS

A little furry animal, a mammal, sticks its pointed whiskery nose out of its burrow and senses the air. Where have all the big animals gone? It can hear no roaring, smell no huge bodies, sense no heavy footsteps. Only small creatures like itself are around now. It scampers from its lair, the first time it has ever done so in broad daylight.

The first mammals evolved at the same time as the dinosaurs, some 220 million years ago. They evolved from the branch of the reptile tree that comprised species with the hole in the skull low down behind the eyes. These were the mammal-like reptiles of Permian and early Triassic times.

The earliest mammal-like reptiles were the pelycosaurs. They had a mixture of mammalian and reptilian characteristics. They had fins on their backs between which skin was stretched to form a sail-like structure. This functioned as a type of body temperature-regulation system. If the animal was feeling cold, it would turn sideways on to the Sun's rays so that blood in the "sail" would absorb heat. If it was too warm, it would face the Sun so that the sail would absorb little heat. This was a forerunner of a mammal's "warm bloodedness," a system that allows an animal to maintain a constant body temperature (usually higher than that of its surroundings). They also had teeth of different sizes and shapes, with each type for a different function, which is a mammal characteristic. But the first pelycosaurs had legs slightly spread out, like those of a crocodile. The later mammal-like reptiles had straight legs that were held beneath the body.

They were also fully warm-blooded and covered in hair. It is even possible that they gave birth to live young.

ALL SHAPES, SIZES AND FORMS

From this stage, it was a short step in evolution to the development of true mammals. It is primarily the arrangement of bones in the lower jaw that separates the advanced mammal-like reptiles from the most primitive true mammals of the Triassic period. The hinge part of each half of a reptile's lower jaw is made up of several bones. That of a mammal's is made up of a

▼Mammals of the late Cretaceous period were small and insignificant. *Zalambdalestes*, left and bottom, probably lived on the forest floor and ate worms and beetles. Its length, including tail, was about 20in. *Deltatheridium*, top right, was an early insect-eating placental species. It probably fed at sunrise and sunset.

single bone, the dentary, with the other bones having evolved into structures of the inner ear.

Throughout the Age of Dinosaurs the mammals were small and shrew- or opossum-like. They probably only came out at night and fed on insects. Then, when the great reptiles died out, they came into their own. With plant-eating dinosaurs gone, species that resembled rhinoceroses and hippopotamuses evolved. The disappearance of meat-eating dinosaurs encouraged the development of wolf- and tiger-like mammals. In the seas,

the plesiosaurs and pliosaurs were replaced by seals and whales. The passing of the pterosaurs, the flying reptiles, resulted in the evolution of aerial mammals, the bats. The smaller mammals also continued to diversify, with the appearance of various shrews, mice and opossums.

MODERN VERSIONS

Today, there are three different groups of mammal. The least highly evolved, and the rarest, are the monotremes, the egg-layers. There are just three species and they are found only in Australia. Two of them are species of echidna or so-called spiny anteater, and the third is the Duck-billed platypus. These are thought to be similar to the mammal-like reptiles, but it is difficult to be sure. Scientists have found very few fossils of monotremes, and certainly not enough to trace out their history.

The second group are the marsupials, the pouched mammals. Of these, the most familiar to us are the kangaroos, wombats, opossums and koala. Marsupial mothers give birth to

their young at a very immature stage and suckle them in a pouch for some time. Nearly all marsupial species – there are over 260 – are confined to Australia. Marsupials were once abundant in South America too, but, except for the surviving opossums, they have since been replaced by the third group of mammals, the placentals.

The placentals are certainly the most abundant of living mammals. There are more than 3,750 species. With the placenta allowing exchange of food, oxygen and carbon dioxide, and waste materials between the blood systems of mother and baby, a young placental mammal grows in the womb until it is at an advanced stage of development. When it is born it is often capable of looking after itself. Newborn antelopes, for example, can run within minutes of birth, and baby whales, born as their mothers swim along, immediately surface to breathe then dive deep.

It appears that at the time of the dinosaurs there were about four other groups of mammals, but all of these have died out.

◀▼ **Four species of extinct mammal** A mammal group that was more important in former times than today is the edentates – anteaters and their relatives. Recently extinct giant forms from South America include *Megatherium* (1), the Giant ground sloth, *Glyptodon* (2), a huge armadillo-like beast, and *Scelidotherium* (3), a large anteater. A much earlier form was *Eomanis* (4), a 50 million-year-old pangolin from Germany.

FOSSIL BIRDS

With ease, a bird stretches its wings and soars in the warm air rising above a forest. In the greenery below smaller birds flit from flower to flower, hovering on their shimmering wings. In a nearby stream, other birds use their wings for swimming and their feathers provide insulation. These creatures are the surviving relatives of the dinosaurs.

Imagine the following steps in evolution. It starts with the smallest of the known dinosaurs, the chicken-sized theropod known as *Compsognathus*. This becomes covered with feathers. The feathers on each side of its slim tail are especially long so that the whole tail forms a paddle-like structure. Then, feathery wings develop on its arms, with long feathers extending past its hands. Its hands, with fingers and claws, remain unchanged. What this produces is an animal called *Archaeopteryx*, the first bird.

It seems that *Archaeopteryx* was the direct descendant of the meat-eating dinosaur line. Some paleontologists even class it as a dinosaur rather than a bird. Apart from its dinosaur-like tail and hands, it also had a reptile's jaws with teeth. It is only the presence of feathers that makes it different from the dinosaurs.

Archaeopteryx lived in late Jurassic times, about 150 million years ago, in the same areas as *Compsognathus*. It shared the skies with such pterosaurs as *Rhamphorhychus* and *Pterodactylus*.

ADAPTED FOR THE AIR
In rocks dating from the late Jurassic to the late Cretaceous period about 70 million years ago, there is a distinct lack of bird fossils. Now and again, in rocks from this timespan the odd bird bone or feather impression is discovered, but the next fossil birds do not really appear before rocks from the late Cretaceous in Kansas State in the center of the United States.

Scientists surmise that between 150 and 65 million years ago the first birds such as *Archaeopteryx* gradually developed all kinds of features that made them better at flying. They developed a deeply keeled breastbone and a wishbone at the collar to anchor the strong flying muscles. The toothed jaws disappeared and a horny beak evolved, which kept down the weight of the head so the animals could balance well in flight. The skeleton became lightened, with the bones developing large hollows. The long and cumbersome lizard-like tail gradually reduced in size and weight and developed the typical bird's tail, which is just a stump supporting an adjustable fan of feathers.

▶ **Some extinct species of bird** Among the most famous fossil birds is the fish-eating *Icththyornis* (**1**) and (**1a**) from the late Cretaceous period. It was a strong flyer. *Hesperornis* (**2**) from rocks of the same period, was totally flightless, but evolved from flying ancestors. *Diatryma* (**3**) stood 7ft tall and hunted small mammals in North America some 50 million years ago.

74

◀▲ The most famous fossil of the first bird *Archaeopteryx* (left) shows it to have been like a small dinosaur covered in feathers. *Archaeopteryx* was the size of a crow and it flew among trees, feeding on insects.

THE FIRST SEABIRDS

Two birds are known from chalk layers in Kansas. The first, called *Icththyornis*, was a small tern-like bird which, like its ancestors, had teeth in its jaws. The second was, in terms of body form, a very peculiar creature. Known as *Hesperornis*, it was as flightless as a penguin and it lived by swimming and diving after fish. It stood 6ft tall, and it too had teeth in its jaws. No sooner had wings evolved than they were lost by birds that adapted to an alternative life-style.

However, birds more like present-day species are known from this time. By the end of the Cretaceous period there were birds that eventually gave rise to all the owls, herons and cormorants familiar to us today.

BIRDS OF ALL TYPES

About 60 million years ago, after the dinosaurs and pterosaurs had died out and the mammals had spread to take over the land, the birds began to take over the sky. Yet flightlessness cropped up again and again throughout bird history and, in some areas, the birds also became the dominant creatures on land. Where plant-eating

▼ A fossil kingfisher, a carnivorous or meat-eating bird like modern kingfishers, found in sedimentary rocks in Provence, southern France. The rocks date from the Oligocene period, between 38 and 25 million years ago.

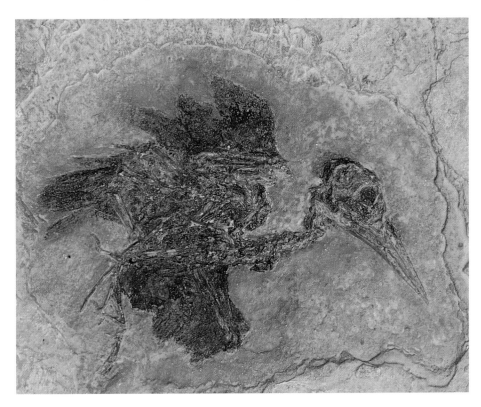

mammals evolved, sometimes meat-eating birds arose before meat-eating mammals.

Representatives of all present-day species of bird became established in the Tertiary period. The fossil record of these animals is not good, though. Bird bones are lightweight and delicate. As a result, after a bird dies its bones tend to be broken easily and become scattered in the earth. The best bird fossils are of shore-living species or seabirds as these are likely to fall into water soon after death and be buried quickly in sediments.

Giant, island-living birds also evolved. On Madagascar, off the southeast coast of Africa, there was a huge ostrich-like creature called *Aepyornis*. On Mauritius, about 300mi further to the east, the turkey-sized dodo evolved. These were all plant-eating birds that became extinct only in recent times when people reached the islands and became the meat-eaters that the islands had lacked naturally.

TERTIARY LIFE

A few million years after the disaster, life abounds again. In the forests are browsers hunted by meat-eaters. The air echoes to the calls of large flying creatures chasing insects. The seas are alive with air-breathing swimming beasts hunting fish. These recently evolved animals are mammals and birds, not reptiles.

The Tertiary period began 65 million years ago when many creatures, including the dinosaurs, died out very quickly. It ended with the coming of the great Ice Age, 2 million years ago. During that time the mammals came to prominence.

Because this is such a recent period of time, and one in which so many familiar animals evolved, including ourselves, the Tertiary is often broken down into much shorter divisions, or epochs. The first three – the Paleocene, Eocene and Oligocene epochs – are usually grouped together as the Paleogene. This was the time when the mammals were unlike those of today. The remaining Miocene and Pliocene epochs together form the Neogene – a time when animal life began to look as it does now.

THE FIRST FLOURISH
All sorts and shapes of mammals evolved in the early Tertiary. Most of them would look very strange to us. It was almost as if every conceivable shape of mammal was being tried out by evolution to see if it worked. As time went on, some of the more unusual creatures died away and there came to the fore the kinds of animals that we would recognize today.

▶ In the Tertiary period the continents moved towards the positions they occupy today. The biggest movement was the closing of a sea, the Tethys, between the southern continents and Europe and Asia.

However most of the land-living mammals of these times were forest-dwellers, browsing the leaves from low-growing bushes.

The climate of the time was warm and generally moist. Forests spread over most of the continents. The continents were still drifting apart and, during the Eocene, North America finally separated from Europe, completing the northern extension of the Atlantic Ocean. By the Oligocene, Australia finally separated from Antarctica, and India ceased to be an island continent and collided with Asia throwing up the vast mountain chain of the Himalayas.

LOWERING SEA LEVELS
Sea levels were generally high during the Paleocene and Eocene. There was a shallow seaway extending from the Arctic through Europe to the region of the modern Mediterranean. This cut off the animals of North America and Europe from those of Asia.

During the next epoch, the Oligocene, there is the first evidence for an ice cap in Antarctica. Water from the world oceans began to be locked up as ice. This, along with the movements of the continents, caused sea levels to fall in all areas of the world.

▶ **Forest-dwelling mammals of the early Tertiary** *Barylambda* (1), a heavy browser; *Ptilodus* (2), a squirrel-like survivor of an ancient group; *Plesiadapis* (3), a lemur ancestor; *Protictis* (4), a hunter; *Meniscotherium* (5), an ancestor of the hoofed animals; *Palaeoryctes* (6), an insect-eater; and *Prodiacodon* (7), an early relative of the hedgehog.

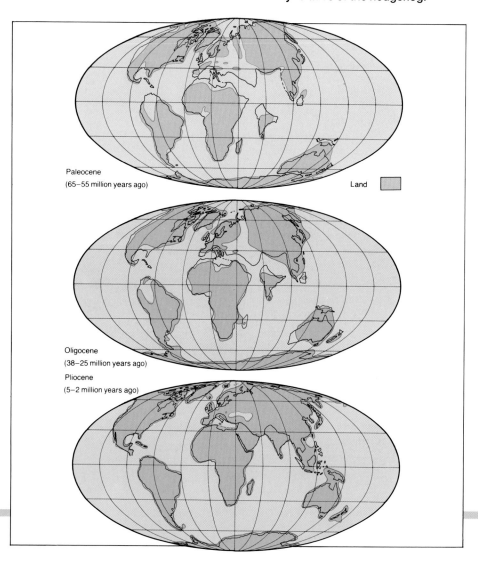

Paleocene
(65–55 million years ago)

Land

Oligocene
(38–25 million years ago)

Pliocene
(5–2 million years ago)

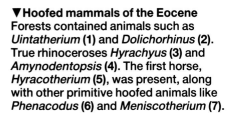

▼**Hoofed mammals of the Eocene**
Forests contained animals such as
Uintatherium (1) and *Dolichorhinus* (2).
True rhinoceroses *Hyrachyus* (3) and
Amynodentopsis (4). The first horse,
Hyracotherium (5), was present, along
with other primitive hoofed animals like
Phenacodus (6) and *Meniscotherium* (7).

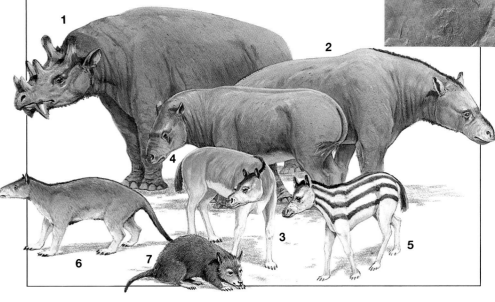

▲A well-preserved skeleton of the first
horse *Hyracotherium* found in coal
deposits in Germany. The animal had its
last meal of leaves preserved in its
stomach cavity.

The shallow seas around the continental shelves and the seaways across the continents dried up. As the climate began to cool more and more over thousands of years, shelf seas reached their smallest extent ever.

IN NORTHERN CONTINENTS

Before the very last part of the Atlantic Ocean opened up in between North America and Europe, the same species of mammal lived in the forests of the two continents. These animals included early hoofed animals, rodents, bats and anteaters. Among them were the small terrier-sized browsing animals, *Hyracotherium*, which were destined to evolve into the horses. In Germany, the remains of the swampy forests of the Eocene epoch now exist as the brown coal deposits that are excavated regularly. In these deposits are found the remains of pangolins and anteaters very

similar to those found in Africa and South America today.

In both early Tertiary Europe and America the primates evolved. The earliest of these were small tree-living lemur-like beasts. From this "birthplace" they spread out into Asia and Africa where, within about 10 million years, they were to become, and stay, important. Their success depended on the evolution of a large brain and the associated heightened senses.

Life was also flourishing in Northern Africa, especially in the region now covered by the Sahara Desert. Here, in misty swamps, wallowed *Moeritherium*, the pig-like ancestor of the elephants, and huge rhinoceros-like beasts such as two-horned *Arsinoitherium*, which browsed on the banks. Small tree-living primates, resembling lemurs, also existed here.

Where various plant-eating animals abound, meat-eaters soon evolve to

hunt them. The meat-eating mammals of the early Tertiary were not the carnivores that we know today. Instead there was a group known as the creodonts. These ranged from little fox-like types such as *Sinopa*, which hunted other small mammals, to big bear-like beasts such as *Sarkastodon*.

SOUTH OF THE EQUATOR

In the southern continents it was the marsupials, the pouched mammals, which were the most important. These probably had their origin in southern Africa while it was still part of the supercontinent Gondwana. From there they spread eastwards to Australia, and westwards to South America.

In South America, most of the plant-eating mammals were primitive hoofed animals. They evolved into camel-, horse-, hippopotamus-, and elephant-like forms. But they were unrelated to the camels and so on living in other parts of the world. The similarities developed by convergent evolution. Meanwhile, most of the carnivorous animals that preyed upon them were marsupials.

Among the carnivorous marsupials was a tiger-like animal, *Thylacosmilus*, which developed huge saber-like teeth in the front of its mouth. It used these to slash into the thick hides of the elephant-like animals. As such, this animal was the marsupial equivalent of the placental Saber-toothed tiger that was to evolve later in the Northern hemisphere. The giant flightless carnivorous birds also existed in South America at this time.

LIFE IN THE OCEANS

In the oceans and shallow seaways of the earliest Tertiary, including the vast Tethys Sea between Africa and the northern continents, the modern ray-finned fish were as important as they

▼**Hoofed mammals of the Oligocene** The rhinoceroses *Indricotherium* (**1**) and *Hyracodon* (**2**), the horse *Mesohippus* (**3**), the camel *Poebrotherium* (**4**), rhinoceros-like *Brontotherium* (**5**), and animals with no modern relatives, for example *Cainotherium* (**6**) and *Merycoidodon* (**7**).

▼**Plant-eaters of the late Eocene** The odd-toed hoofed mammals, the group to which the horses and rhinoceroses belong, evolved in the Eocene forests of North America. These early forms ate leaves rather than grass and included rhinoceros-like *Eotitanops* (top left). *Paleomoropus* (top right) was like a horse with claws. *Heptodon* (bottom right) was an early tapir. *Metamylodon* (bottom left) was a rhinoceros. *Hyracotherium* (center) was the first horse.

are today. Aquatic mammals evolved to hunt them. Among these, the earliest whales were long and sea serpent-like. The other fish-eating marine mammals, the seals and the sea lions, did not evolve until late Tertiary times. Although species in these two groups look similar, they are unrelated. The seals evolved from otter-like ancestors, while the sea lions all developed from dogs.

LIVING IN THE OPEN

About half way through the Tertiary the climate began to change. Cooler drier weather spread across the continents. The worldwide forests died back and, for the first time, grasslands spread all across the landscape. As always, a change in environment resulted in a change in animal life.

Grass is a very tough substance. Eating it is like eating sandpaper. A grass-eating animal has to evolve very sturdy teeth and a new type of digestive system, one that can extract the goodness from grass.

With no trees on the grassland, danger can be seen coming from a long way off. But there are no hiding places, and so a grass-eating animal needs to be able to run away quickly if a meat-eater approaches. With these pressures selecting those animals best-adapted to their surroundings, the spread of the grasslands encouraged the evolution of hoofed animals such as horses, antelopes and cattle.

Meat-eaters able to stalk prey and run fast evolved to feed upon highly mobile grass-eaters. The modern carnivores, including the dogs and cats, gradually developed.

THE END OF ISOLATION

Towards the end of the Tertiary period, a bridge of land was established between the continents of North America and South America, and the grassland animals of the north swept south and vice versa. Those from the north proved to be more adaptable, and the bizarre southern beasts, such as the Giant ground sloth, were wiped out.

The formation of this land link, along with the closure of the Tethys Sea between Africa and Europe, led to a cooling of the Earth's climate which became more extreme towards the end of the Tertiary period.

►**Some large North American mammals of the Oligocene** Plant-eating animals able to run fast included *Brontotherium* (1); *Poebrotherium* (2), an early camel; *Merycoidodon* (3), one of the early cattle-like species; *Archaeotherium* (4) and *Daeodon* (5), pig-like species; *Metamynodon* (6), a rhino; *Mesohippus* (7), a plains horse; and *Leptomeryx* (8), an antelope look-alike. Meat-eaters included *Hyaenodon* (9), and *Amphicyon* (10), a dog-like bear.

QUATERNARY LIFE

A cold gust of wind blasts a flurry of snow down from the gray sky beyond the ice wall. A great beast, kept warm by its thick fur, crunches its way across a gravelly stream bed. It is heading towards the sparse grazing among the stunted willow trees on the far bank. Its huge curving tusks push the snow away from the grasses, and it sweeps up a bunch of stems in its trunk and eats them.

Throughout the Tertiary period the climates on Earth became increasingly cooler. Ice caps built up on the Antarctic continent and on Greenland, and the almost land-locked Arctic Ocean became covered in a layer of ice. These vast masses of ice became thicker and spread outwards towards the warmer latitudes. Eventually, as the Tertiary slipped into the Quaternary period about 2 million years ago, the deteriorating weather conditions produced the "Ice Age."

COLD THEN COOL
The Ice Age was not a single continuous period of cold. Glaciers swept southwards several times across North America, Europe and northern Asia, and an equal number of times they retreated again. Partial melting of the ice occurred during spells in which the climate was warmer than it is today. Glaciation then thawing happened about twenty times, each phase lasting several thousand years.

Each time the ice advanced, sea levels fell, producing areas of dry land that were once at the bottom of the continental shelves. When the ice melted and retreated, the sea levels rose once more. In the far north, where the ice was thickest, this effect was magnified by the fact that the weight of the glaciers pushed the land downwards.

Lands in the Southern hemisphere were also affected, with glaciers sweeping down from the Andes in the southern part of South America, and the Antarctic ice cap reaching out much further than it does today.

WILDLIFE OF THE NORTH
As had happened many times before in evolution, in the Quaternary animal life developed to accommodate the new environment. Under cold conditions, a large animal does better than a small one. Its greater volume of body keeps in the heat more efficiently. Thick layers of fat and a woolly coat evolve as insulation. As a result, during

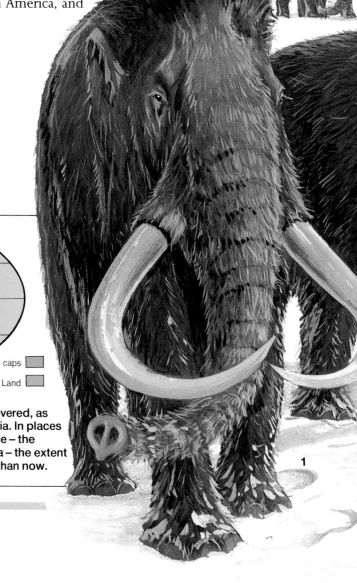

1

Pleistocene
2 million years ago

Ice caps
Land

▲ The Quaternary Ice Age took place during the Pleistocene epoch. At their greatest extent the ice sheets spread down through Canada to the United States. Nearly all of the British Isles and Scandinavia were covered, as were great areas of Siberia. In places that are still gripped by ice – the Himalayas and Antarctica – the extent of ice was much greater than now.

the Ice Age big hairy animals such as woolly mammoths, woolly rhinoceroses and cave bears gradually developed.

These animals would not have lived on the ice caps themselves. Most of them would have roamed in herds across the tundra, the marshy area of stunted trees and mosses that now exist in the far north of Canada and Siberia. In the Quaternary, tundra would have covered a great deal of northern Europe as well.

▼**Cold climate animals of Europe in the Quaternary period** These included *Mammuthus* (1), the woolly mammoth; *Coelodonta* (2), a woolly rhinoceros; *Ursus spelaeus* (3), the cave bear; *Equus ferus* (4), one of the Ice Age horses; and *Panthera leo spelaea* (5), the cave lion, a subspecies of the modern lion, *P. leo*. The cave bear was of the same genus, *Ursus*, as modern bears, but a different species, *U. spelaeus*. Despite its size and ferocious appearance it ate seeds and shoots.

CHANGES IN PLANT LIFE

The plants of the Pleistocene Ice Age did not evolve in the same dramatic ways as did the animals. The forests and grasslands spread north and south according to the climate, and most of today's species appeared quickly and did not change into new kinds. Even during the coldest spells of the times, there was still a belt of tropical forest around the equator. However, this belt was much narrower than it is today, with the grasslands to the north and south encroaching on it.

The times that the ice retreated and the climate became milder are known as the interglacials. Animals that we associate with warm environments were found much further north than they, or their descendants, are today. For example, pond turtles, which nowadays are most common in tropical and sub-tropical regions, lived in the lakes of Scandinavia.

IN SOUTHERN CONTINENTS

During the warm spells there was much forest in South America, but this was replaced by grassland when the cold times arrived again. Large animals such as the Giant ground sloths and glyptodonts – armadillo-

▲ Cave paintings represent eye witness accounts of late Ice Age animals. In Lascaux, central France, these 20,000-year-old paintings show reindeer, bulls and horses.

◄ Giants of the Pleistocene During the Ice Age oil seeping to the surface of the land in the region of modern Los Angeles formed tar pits that trapped the animals of the time. These included *Equus* (1), the modern horse; *Mammuthus imperator* (2), one of the biggest mammoths; *Smilodon* (3), a Saber-toothed tiger; *Glossotherium* (4), a Giant ground sloth; *Capromeryx* (5), a prongbuck; *Bison antiquus* (6), a Giant bison; *Canis dirus* (7), a wolf; and *Homotherium* (8), a slow-moving dagger-toothed cat.

like creatures the size of automobiles – evolved. With the huge bridge of land between North and South America firmly established, some of these strange animals migrated northwards and flourished in what is now the United States.

Large animals also evolved in Australia, from the marsupial species that existed there. A wombat as big as a hippopotamus, known as *Diprotodon*, grazed the Australian plains, as did *Procoptodon*, a giant kangaroo as large as the South American ground sloths. Marsupial hunters lived there too.

ANOTHER MAJOR CHANGE

As the Pleistocene epoch merged into the Holocene epoch – the scientific term for modern times – about 20,000 years ago, there was another mass extinction. This saw an end to the mammoths, the woolly rhinoceroses, the Giant ground sloth of South and North America, and the big marsupials of Australia.

The dying out of so many species coincided with the last retreat of the glaciers and the coming of warm weather. So the cause of the mass extinction may have been the changing climate or it may have been the coming of a new creature. This new creature was an efficient hunter. It worked in cooperative groups and had the ability to make and use weapons. It was the first human.

Human beings had spread from the Old World (Africa and Asia) across the bridge of dry land that once linked present-day Alaska and Siberia and is now the Bering Strait. By 30,000 years ago they had occupied all of North America. By 12,000 years ago, they had traveled deep into South America. Elsewhere in the world, by 32,000 years ago, they had crossed the East Indies chain of islands and had reached Australia. Hunting by early human beings was probably not the only cause of the Ice Age extinctions, but it was certainly a major cause.

FOSSIL HUMANS

An ape-like creature scampers on all fours through the grass to food in the next thicket. The animal stands up, enabling it to see farther and allowing the wind to cool its body. It prefers this position but cannot hold it for long without getting tired. It has not evolved for this kind of stance – yet.

One of the groups of mammals to evolve and spread across the continents at the beginning of the Tertiary period was the primates – the lemurs, monkeys and apes, which includes ourselves, the human species.

The first primates were little creatures like the modern tree shrews, mouse-sized beasts that scampered along branches sniffing out insects, seeds, fruits and birds' eggs. As they became better adapted for a tree-living way of life, they developed long fingers and toes that enabled them to cling to twigs, and eyes that focused forwards to help them to judge the distances between the branches. Animals that resembled the modern lemurs and tarsiers gradually evolved.

APES ARRIVE

These so-called prosimians (meaning before the simians, or apes) were very successful in the forests of the early Tertiary. By Pliocene times, 5 to 2 million years ago, ape-like creatures existed. *Ramapithecus*, from Europe, India and Africa, seems to have been close to the common ancestor of the apes and humans. It was definitely a tree-living animal, but it probably spent some of its time on the ground.

OUT OF THE TREES

The drying climates of East Africa some 3 million years ago caused the forests to dwindle, and a more open woodland landscape then developed. A ground-dwelling ape, *Australopithecus* evolved.

Different species of *Australopithecus* were present in the Pliocene epoch. The earliest to evolve was *A. afarensis*. It was no bigger than a medium-sized monkey, but the skeleton shows that it could walk with an upright gait and it had a larger brain than any other creature. This allowed it to see over

◀ *Ramapithecus*, from 8 million years ago, had a flat human-like face with human-like teeth and jaws. Occasionally, it may have left the safety of the trees and used sticks and stones for defense.

▼ The evolutionary tree of modern humans is not yet clear. However, it seems likely that *Ramapithecus*, or something closely resembling it, gave rise to *Australopithecus*, and the more adaptable species of this gave rise to the genus *Homo*, from which we evolved.

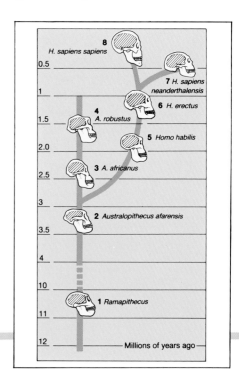

▲ *Australopithecus afarensis* lived in Ethiopia and Tanzania, in open country that it journeyed across in family groups. It would have walked upright but with a slight stoop. Its brain capacity was about a third of that of ours.

▶ *Australopithecus robustus* was a strict vegetarian. It was well adapted to a gathering and browsing existence in the thorn forests of East Africa and did not evolve any further. It was succeeded by the more adaptable *A. africanus*.

long grass and to enable the wind to keep it cool in the heat of the day. It also freed the forelimbs so that that hands could be used for purposes other than clinging to branches.

Australopithecus then evolved into two main ancestral types. The first, represented by the species *A. robustus*, lived on a diet of just seeds and nuts. This somewhat gorilla-like creature developed no further. The second, which included the species *A. africanus*, adopted a more omnivorous diet. It could eat meat as well as plant material, and in order to obtain the meat, individuals banded together to hunt animals or chase other animals away from their kill. A social way of life was beginning to form.

◄*Homo habilis*, or "Handy man," was the first being to make tools. These were mostly pebbles with a roughly chipped blade along one edge. Its remains were first found in the famous Olduvai Gorge in Tanzania, East Africa.

OUR PROBABLE ANCESTORS

During the early part of the Ice Age, about 2 million years ago, the genus *Homo* evolved. The earliest species that we know about lived in Tanzania at about the same time as the more advanced *Australopithecus* species. This was *Homo habilis*, or "handy man." It was quite distinct from *Australopithecus* in that it had the ability not just to pick up sticks and stones and use them as tools, but to reason that tools were needed to solve certain problems and make the tools in the first place. It seems that *H. habilis* built shelters as well, and may have had some form of rudimentary speech.

OUT OF AFRICA

The next species to evolve was *H. erectus*, or "upright man." As the name suggests, it had a fully upright stance. It was able to build shelters of brushwood supported on wooden frames and anchored by stones. Its tools and weapons were superior to anything its predecessors made. More important, though, is that *H. erectus* used fire.

With such knowledge and abilities, *H. erectus* spread all over the world about 500,000 years ago. Remains of its settlements have been found in parts of Africa, Europe and in the Far East, especially in China and Java.

THINKING MAN

With the onset of the coldest spells of the Ice Age, the modern species of human evolved. This is called *H. sapiens*, "wise man" or "thinking man,"

◄*Homo erectus*, or "Upright man", had tools and weapons that included spears, blades and choppers, made from wood, stone and bone. It used fire to defend its home, to scare animals into ambushes, and to cook food.

▲ *Homo sapiens neanderthalensis*, "Neanderthal man", had a broad head with a bulbous nose and prominent eyebrows. It had a rudimentary religious culture shown by the careful way in which it buried the dead of its tribes.

because of its large brain and its ability to use it for reasoning.

Originally, there were two sub-species. The first evolved about 250,000 years ago, and lived, as far as we know, in Europe, northern Africa and central Asia. Remains of this human were first found in the Neander valley in Germany, from which its name H. *sapiens neanderthalensis*, "Neanderthal man," is taken. It had a complex society. This subspecies died out about 30,000 years ago.

Its cousin, H. *sapiens sapiens*, evolved a little later. As the Ice Age waned, this subspecies developed farming and animal husbandry. From then on, its history is that of our own civilization.

▶ *Homo sapiens sapiens*. The earliest modern human is called "Cro-Magnon man" after a site in France in which its remains were found. More efficient food-gathering techniques allowed him time to develop cave painting.

GLOSSARY

Adaptation Features of an animal's body or life-style that suit it to its environment.

Adaptive radiation The development of one group of animals into a number of different groups each adopting a unique way of life in their different niches.

Adult A fully developed animal that is mature and capable of breeding.

Amphibians Animals such as frogs and toads, which have a larval stage dependent on water and an an adult stage that lives on land.

Aquatic Living for much, if not all, of the time in the water.

Bacterium Extremely small one-celled creature with a very simple nucleus.

Behavior Any of an animal's actions, rather than its structure.

Browser An animal that feeds on the shoots, leaves and bark of shrubs and trees.

Camouflage Colors, patterns and associated behaviours of animals that allow them to blend with their surroundings and remain undetected by predators.

Canopy The upper living layer of a forest formed by the intermingling of branches and leaves.

Carnivore An animal that feeds on other animals.

Carrion Meat from a dead animal.

Climate The average weather conditions in a region.

Colonization The process whereby new species take over a new habitat.

Competition The contest between two or more species over such things as space and food.

Conifers Trees that bear cones. Their needle-like leaves usually stay on the trees all year.

Convergent evolution The development of similar features or shapes in unrelated animals to adapt them to similar ecological niches,

Cooperation The assistance of one animal by another where both gain. For example, many watching eyes make it easier for herd animals to spot predators.

Creationism The belief that all life was created in its present form and has not subsequently changed.

Culture A set of patterns of behavior that are reproduced by learning. They are often passed from generation to generation.

Deciduous trees Trees that shed their leaves seasonally, usually in the autumn or fall.

Desert An area with low rainfall.

Display A pattern of things done by one animal that gives information to other animals. It may be seen or heard. Greeting, threatening or courtship may involve displays between animals.

Dominance The ability of an animal to take precedence over another for food, mates or good resting positions. Dominance may be, but is not necessarily, achieved by fighting.

Dormancy A state of deep sleep in which all body processes slow down to reduce energy consumption so that an animal can survive for long periods without feeding.

Ecology The study of plants and animals in relation to their environment.

Environment The surroundings of an organism, including both the living and non-living world.

Era An interval of geological time, comprising several periods.

Extinction The complete loss of a species, locally or worldwide.

Family The division of zoological classification coming between Order and Genus.

Fauna Animal life.

Feral Living in the wild. It refers to domesticated species or to animals that have escaped from captivity.

Flora Plant life.

Foraging Going in search of food.

Genes The units of inheritance which are transmitted from generation to generation and control the development of an individual.

Genus The division of animal classification below Family and above Species.

Grazer An animal that feeds on grass.

Habitat The surroundings in which an animal lives, including the plant life, other animals, the physical landscape and climate.

Herbivore An animal that eats plants.

Hibernation A state of dormancy in winter. In mammals it may involve cooling of the body and slowing of the body processes such as breathing and beating of the heart.

Hoarding Hiding food away in a store or cache to which the animal later returns.

Hominid A human-like animal belonging to the evolutionary line leading to humans today.

Homology A character in two or more animals that can be traced back to a single character in the common ancestor. The flipper of the seal and the wing of the bat are homologous, both developing from the forelimbs of the ancestral mammal.

Incubation Period during which an animal keeps an egg warm allowing the embryo inside to grow.

Insectivore An insect eater.

Instinct Behavior that is "built into" an animal; that portion of behavior which is inherited not learned.

Intelligence The capacity that enables an individual to learn tasks, reason and solve problems.

Invertebrates Animals without a backbone.

Mammal A class of animals whose females have mammary glands which produce milk on which they feed their young.

Marine Living in or on the sea.

Marsupial A class of primitive mammals whose females give birth to very underdeveloped young and raise them (usually) in a pouch.

Migration Long-distance journeys made by animals, particularly regular seasonal movements, as between nesting and wintering grounds.

Mimicry (1) Resemblance in shape, color or pattern between two animals, that may give one or both an advantage. For example some harmless flies mimic wasps. (2) Imitation of behavior, as when one bird mimics the song of another.

Monotremes Primitive mammals that lay eggs. The platypus and the echidna are the only living monotremes.

Mutation A sudden change in a creature's genes, resulting in offspring that are somehow different.

Natural selection The process whereby individuals whith the most appropriate adaptations are more successful than others, and hence survive to produce more offspring.

Niche The particular way of life of a species in a certain habitat, for example a leaf-eater in a rain forest.

Omnivore An animal that eats both animal and plant material.

Paleontology The study of fossils.

Parallel evolution The development of similar features in related groups of animals, brought about independently by the similarity of conditions in the areas inhabited by each group.

Parasitism One species living on or inside another one, feeding at the host's expense.

Photosynthesis The process by which green plants are able to make their own food. They use the energy in sunlight and chlorophyll in their leaves to combine carbon dioxide (from the air) with water (from the ground) to make sugar.

Placentals Mammals in which the young are held inside the mother's womb until quite advanced, being nourished from the mother's blood supply by a placenta. Most modern mammals are placentals.

Population A separate group of animals of the same species, as for example, in a particular geographical area. Physical barriers usually prevent different populations from mixing.

Predator An animal that hunts other live animals as its prey.

Prey An animal that is hunted.

Reptiles Cold-blooded animals with a scaly skin, such as snakes, lizards, crocodiles and tortoises.

Rodent A mammal belonging to the animal order that includes rats, mice and squirrels.

Scavenger An animal that eats dead animals and plants, perhaps including decaying matter.

Species The division of animal classification below Genus; a group of animals of the same structure that can breed together.

Stratigraphy The study of the composition, distribution, origin and succession of rock strata.

Symbiosis An association between two species in which both gain some form of benefit.

Taxonomy The study of the classification of organisms.

Terrestrial Spending most of the time on the ground.

Territory The area in which an animal or group of animals lives and which it defends against intruders.

Vertebrates Animals with a backbone.

INDEX

Page numbers in normal "roman" type indicate text entries. **Bold** numbers refer to captions to illustrations. Many of the entries refer to general animal types and not to individual species. Where the text relates to a species, the Latin name of that animal is given in brackets after the common name.

FURTHER READING

Berry, R. J. and Hallam, A. (eds) (1986), *The Encyclopedia of Animal Evolution*, Facts on File, New York.

Bonner J. T. (ed) (1981), *Evolution and Development*, Springer-Verlag, Berlin.

Bowler, P. (1983), *The Eclipse of Darwinism*, Johns Hopkins University Press, Baltimore.

Bowler, P. J. (1984), *Evolution. The History of an Idea*, University of California Press, Berkeley.

Brown, J. L. (1975), *The Evolution of Behavior*, Norton, New York.

Browne, J. L. (1983), *The Secular Ark*, Yale University Press, New Haven.

Cherfas, J. (ed) (1982), *Darwin up to Date*, New Scientist, London.

Dobzhansky, T. (1937, 3rd edn 1951), *Genetics and the Origin of Species*, Columbia University Press, New York. (Revised as *Genetics of the Evolutionary Process*, 1970)

Eicher, D. L., McAlester, A. L. and Rottman, M. L. (1984), *The History of the Earth's Crust*, Prentice-Hall, Englewood Cliffs, New Jersey.

Futuyama, D. J. and Slatkin, M. (eds) (1983), *Coevolution*, Sinauer, Sunderland, Mass.

Futuyama, D. J. (1983), *Science on Trial*, Pantheon, New York.

Gillespie, N. C. (1979), *Charles Darwin and the Problem of Creation*, University of Chicago Press, Chicago and London.

Gould, S. J. (1977), *Ever Since Darwin*. Norton, New York.

Gould, S. J. (1980), *The Panda's Thumb*, Norton, New York and London.

Gould, S. J. (1983), *Hen's teeth and Horse's Toes*, Norton, New York.

Grayson, D. K. (1983), *The Establishment of Human Antiquity*, Academic Press, New York.

Hallam, A. (ed) (1977), *Patterns of Evolution as Illustrated by the Fossil Record*, Elsevier, Amsterdam.

Hull, D. L. (1973), *Darwin and His Critics*, Harvard University Press, Cambridge, Mass.

Leakey, R. E. (1981), *The Making of Mankind*, Michael Joseph, London.

Mason, I. L. (ed) (1984), *Evolution of Domesticated Animals*, Longman, London and New York.

Maynard Smith J, (1958, 3rd edn 1975), *The Theory of Evolution*, Penguin, Harmondsworth.

Maynard Smith J. (ed) (1982), *Evolution Now: A Century After Darwin*. Macmillan, London.

Mayr, E. (1982), *The Growth of Biological Thought*, Belknap, Cambridge, Mass and London.

Mayr, E. and Provine, W.B. (1980), *The Evolutionary Synthesis*, Harvard University Press, Cambridge, Mass.

Morris, H. M. (ed) (1974), *Scientific Creationism, Creation-Life*. San Diego, California.

Nei, M. and Koehn, R. K. (eds) (1983), *Evolution of Genes and Proteins*, Sinauer, Sunderland, Mass.

Raup, D. M. and Jablonski, D. (eds) (1986), *Pattern and Process in the History of Life*, Springer-Verlag, Berlin.

Raup, D. M. and Stanley, S. M. (1978), *Principles of Paleontology* (2nd edn), Freeman, San Francisco.

Ruse, M. (1982), *Darwinism Defended*, Addison-Wesley, Reading, Mass.

Savage, D. E. and Russell, D. E. (1983), *Mammalian Palaeofaunas of the World*, Addison-Wesley, Reading, Mass.

Scientific American (1978), *Evolution*, Freeman, San Francisco.

Sibley, R. M. and Smith, R. H. (eds) (1985), *Behavioural Ecology: Ecological Consequences of Adaptive Behaviour*, Blackwell, Oxford.

Sober, E. (ed) (1984), *Conceptual Issues in Evolutionary Biology*, M.I.T., Cambridge, Mass.

Stanley, S. M. (1981), *The New Evolutionary Timetable*, Basic, New York.

Stanley, S. M. (1986), *Earth and Life through Time*, Freeman, San Francisco.

Stauffer, R. C. (ed) (1975), *Charles Darwin's Natural Selection*, Cambridge University Press, Cambridge.

Taylor, T. N. (1981), *Palaeobotany: An Introduction to Fossil Plant Biology*, Mcgraw-Hill, London.

ACKNOWLEDGMENTS

Picture credits

Key t top, b bottom, c center, l left, r right.

Abbreviations:
ANT Australian Nature Transparencies. BCL Bruce Coleman Ltd. BMNH British Museum (Natural History). NHPA Natural History Photographic Agency. OSF Oxford Scientific Films. SAL Survival Anglia Ltd. SPL Science Photo Library.

4 SPL/Dr Gopal Murti. 6 Tate Gallery, London. 7t Francis Danby: The Flood, Tate Gallery, London. 7b Andromeda Archive. 8t BBC Hulton Picture Library. 8cl Geological Survey, London. 8br Geological Museum/BMNH. 9t Mansell Collection. 9b Mary Evans Picture Library. 10 Dougal Dixon. 11t Maurice Nimmo. 11b Dr J.S. Shelton. 12-13 Hayward Art Group. 14,15t Hayward Art Group. 15b A.J. Charig. 16bl Imitor. 16bc Simon Driver. 16cr Zefa. 16br Novosti Press Agency. 17 SPL/J. Koivula. 18t Sinclair Stammers. 18br SPL/Sinclair Stammers. 19t Zefa/C. Maher. 19b Simon Driver. 20 Zefa. 21 Geological Museum/BMNH. 22-23 Oxford Illustrators Ltd. 23tl Sio Photo. 23br S.W. Fox. 23r Spectrum Colour Library. 24tr, bl Simon Driver. 24br BCL/Jeff Simon. 25tl BCL. 25tr,b Simon Driver. 25br C. A. Henley. 26 Richard Orr. 27c BCL. 27b Simon Driver. 28-29 Richard Orr. 30-31 Denys Ovenden. 32bl,br Dr L.M. Cook. 33 Trevor Boyer. 34-35 Coral Mula. 36-37 Priscilla Barrett. 37tr SAL/J. Foott. 38tr Sinclair Stammers. 38bl Andromeda Oxford Ltd. 39t M.R. Walter. 39b OSF/Ronald Templeton. 40b Dr R. Goldring. 40-41 Michael Long. 41t S. Conway-Morris. 42 Geoscience Features Ltd. 43tl BCL/F. Sauer. 43tr Institute of Geological Science, London. 43b Biofotos/H. Angel. 44-45 Michael Long. 45 Andromeda Oxford Ltd. 46,47t,b T. Morris. 48l SAL/Jeff Foott. 48r J. Fuller. 49 P. Morris. 51 Michael Long. 52 T. Morris. 53t Hayward Art Group. 53b ANT/A. Dennis. 54-55 Chris Forsey. 56 T. Morris. 57c P.J. McCabe. 57b T. Morris. 58t Simon Driver. 58-59 Michael Long. 60t BCL/Norman Tomalin. 60c BCL/J. & D Bartlett. 60b P. Morris. 61b P. Morris. 62-63 Michael Long. 63 Andromeda Oxford Ltd. 64-65 Chris Forsey. 66-67 Chris Forsey. 68bl Andromeda Oxford Ltd. 68br OSF/Kathie Atkinson.68-69,70-71,72 Michael Long. 73t Novosti Picture Agency. 73b Priscilla Barrett. 74 Tony Maynard. 75tl BCL. 75b BCL/John Cancalosi. 76 Andromeda Oxford Ltd. 77,78tl Michael Long. 78tr Dr Jens Lorenz Franzen. 79tr,b, 80-81 Michael Long. 82 Hayward Art Group. 82-83, 84-85b Michael Long. 84-85t Musée du Périgord, Périgueux. 86l Richard Hook. 86r Oxford Illustrators Ltd. 87,88-89 Richard Hook.

Artwork © Priscilla Barrett 1986